SLIDE RULE

THE AUTHOR

Calvin C. Bishop is a professional electrical engineer with a varied background of mechanical and electrical experience. He is a graduate of Syracuse University and also studied at Buffalo State Teachers College and Canisius College. His early experience included shop work with the General Electric Company. For many years he was head of the departments of drafting and design and electricity at the Buffalo Technical High School. He has taught at the University of Buffalo, the Y. M. C. A. Institute of Technology, and the Engineering Society of Buffalo. He has held positions with several companies as electrical designer and consulting engineer. In 1955 he retired from California Institute of Technology, where he was senior design engineer.

Mr. Bishop is the author of *Electrical Drafting and Design*, *Alternating Currents for Technical Students*, and several articles for educational and engineering bulletins. At present he is engaged in engineering and technical writing, specializing in the development of inventions and projects.

SLIDE RULE

A Practical Guide to Its Use
With Examples, Problems, Answers

Calvin C. Bishop

Third Edition

BARNES & NOBLE, INC. NEW YORK

Publishers • Booksellers • Founded 1874

©

Third Edition, 1955
Copyright 1947, 1952, 1955, by

BARNES & NOBLE, Inc.

All rights reserved

Cover design by
DAVID and ADELAIDE WURSTER

Formerly published under the title:
Practical Use of the Slide Rule

Printed in the United States of America

PREFACE

The purpose of this book is to explain by easy and reliable methods how one can use the slide rule to perform accurate mathematical calculations. The author has used these methods successfully for more than twenty years, and has found them suitable both for classroom work and for home study.

Part One gives a detailed exposition of the use of the Mannheim and Polyphase Slide Rule. The salient features are:

a. Explanations for each operation are logically developed in a series of well-defined steps.

b. Each operation is illustrated with at least one diagram which gives the setting for the problem discussed.

c. Each topic is followed by many problems as a drill.

d. A special system is presented for locating decimal places in many different operations.

Part Two presents charts of other well-known slide rules used for special operations. Sample settings for each type of operation are explained opposite the chart of the rule being used.

The Appendix gives supplementary problems for drill, as well as many practical problems covering topics often met in mechanical, civil, electrical, and chemical engineering. Answers to all problems are given; the author has become convinced by long experience in teaching slide rule that this is advisable. Without such answers, a student will often make wrong settings, and, having no way to check himself, will acquire a wrong technique which later will have to be discarded. By working towards definite answers, and repeating the operations several times if necessary to obtain the correct answer, he can discover and correct his errors in procedure. The answers in this book have been worked out with great accuracy, using "old-fashioned arithmetic" and logarithms, and they are given to the nearest reading on the slide rule.

The author is confident that by following the methods of this book, with reasonable practice each day, a student can learn to perform the ordinary operations of multiplication, division, reciprocals, powers, and roots in about two weeks. If he has a fair working knowledge of trigonometry and logarithms, he can solve rather difficult problems on those topics in another week. Practice on the many problems (with answers) will develop speed and accuracy in the use of the slide rule.

It has been found by experience that learning the slide rule can be made most interesting by two or more students' working together and making slide rule practice a game. The winner must excel in speed and accuracy. The problems in this book are arranged particularly for such a game. Answers are to be written in lead pencil in the boxes in each student's book, and then checked with the answers in the answer section. The penciled answers may then be erased and second and third tests run.

The slide rule is not an instrument to be studied and then put aside. It should be kept handy like a pen or pencil and used whenever possible, for it is quick and has an accuracy comparable to that of many of the instruments with which engineering measurements are made.

Calvin C. Bishop
Pasadena, California

ACKNOWLEDGMENTS

The author is indebted to several of his friends for suggestions and for problems: to Mr. John W. Greenwood and Dr. M. Ernest Chriswall for problems on mensuration from their *Handbook of Elementary Technical Mathematics;* to Mr. Lester A. Cherry, Consulting Engineer, for problems in thermodynamics; to Mr. Clark Suor for problems in civil engineering; and to Mr. William Block for problems in chemistry. He is also grateful to Miss Mary M. Brown for assistance in checking the answers to many of the problems in the book.

CONTENTS

PART ONE

Use of the POLYPHASE Slide Rule

Chapter   Page

I   Introduction.................................. 3

II   Multiplication, Division, and Proportion........ 8

III   Finding the Place for the Decimal Point....... 12

IV   CI Scale and Folded Scales CF and DF.......... 22

V   Slide Rule Operations Involving Squares and Square Roots.............................. 30

VI   Slide Rule Operations Involving Cubes and Cube Roots................................... 35

VII   Slide Rule Operations Involving the Common Trigonometric Functions..................... 41

VIII   Logarithms and Their Application to the Slide Rule   47

PART TWO

Well-Known Slide Rules Explained by Charts and Sample Settings

*POLYPHASE Slide Rule..................... 55

*POLYPHASE DUPLEX TRIG Slide Rule... 56

*LOG LOG DUPLEX TRIG Slide Rule........ 62

*LOG LOG DUPLEX VECTOR Slide Rule... 74

**POST VERSALOG Slide Rule.............. 88

LANGSNER INDUSTRIAL Slide Rule...... 96

APPENDIX

A   Problems for Drill............................ 105

B   Practical Problems........................... 113

        Problems in Areas........................... 113

        Problems in Areas and Volumes.............. 116

        Problems in Trigonometry.................... 120

        Problems in Mechanics...................... 123

        Problems in Civil Engineering................. 127

        Problems in Chemistry....................... 130

        Problems in Electrical Engineering............ 134

        Problems in Thermodynamics................ 138

        Answers..................................... 144

*Trade-Mark of KEUFFEL & ESSER CO.

** Trade-Mark of FREDERICK POST CO.

PART ONE

USE OF THE
POLYPHASE SLIDE RULE

CHAPTER I

INTRODUCTION

DESCRIPTION OF THE SLIDE RULE

The slide rule is an instrument for performing mathematical operations quickly and easily and yet with sufficient accuracy for very many engineering computations. In theory it is possible to make a slide rule that will compute to almost any degree of accuracy but practically the 10 inch slide rule is the best one known and the most widely used. A 20 inch rule may be obtained for desk use, and a 5 inch pocket rule for approximate calculations.

All slide rules have three parts: the body or rule proper, the slide, and the indicator or runner. These parts are clearly labeled in the cut of Fig. 1 which shows a modern slide rule known as the "POLYPHASE DUPLEX DECITRIG slide rule."

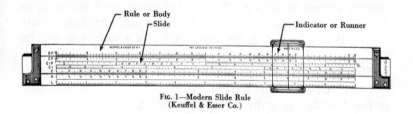

FIG. 1—Modern Slide Rule
(Keuffel & Esser Co.)

CALCULATIONS ONE CAN MAKE ON THE SLIDE RULE

The ordinary slide rule will enable you to:

(a) Multiply	(h) Find Sines
(b) Divide	(i) Find Cosines
(c) Find Reciprocals	(j) Find Tangents
(d) Square Numbers	(k) Find Cotangents
(e) Find Square Root	(l) Find Logarithms
(f) Cube Numbers	(m) Find Fractional Powers
(g) Find Cube Root	(n) Find Fractional Roots

3

Many slide rules have special scales for operations other than those listed above; as a person familiar with the fundamental operations of the ordinary slide rule can readily learn to use these by himself, some of these special scales are described in Part II.

THE SCALES AND HOW TO READ THEM

The scales on the front of the rule are known as the A, B, CI, C, and D scales. Some rules have another scale known as the K scale on the front; others have the K scale on the side of the rule.

The A scale is on the body of the rule and consists of two sections each one-half the length of the rule. Both sections are similarly divided into ten parts or main divisions but for reasons to be explained later, the divisions are not all the same size. The left-hand or first section of the A scale starts with a rather large main division at the left-hand end of the rule and ends with a much smaller division at the center of the rule. This section is numbered from 1 to 10. The right-hand or second section of the A scale has the same sized divisions as the left-hand section but these divisions are numbered from 10 to 100. The reason for this system of numbering will be explained under "Squaring" and "Square Root."

The B scale is the same as the A scale but is on the slide.

The C scale is on the slide and is twice as long as each section of the A scale. It is divided into ten main divisions and numbered from 1 to 10.

The D scale is the same as the C scale but is on the body of the rule.

The CI scale is on the slide and is divided and numbered like the C scale. The CI scale, however, is "inverted"; that is, it is read from the right towards the left.

The K scale consists of three sections, each a third the length of the rule. All three sections are similarly divided into ten parts. The left-hand or first section reads from 1 to 10; the center or second section reads from 10 to 100; and the right-hand or third section reads from 100 to 1000. This special numbering will be explained under "Cubing" and "Cube Root."

Since the divisions on the above scales are large near the low numbers marked on the scales, and small near the high numbers, it is not practical to subdivide the main divisions the same throughout the length of the scales. A large number of subdivisions that could easily be read, say between 1 and 2 on the C scale, would be so crowded together between 9 and 10 that they would be very difficult to read.

The A, B, CI, C, and D scales start with 1 instead of 0 as we are used to in reading ordinary rules and electric meters. In reading these scales between 1 and 2, we first read 1, then the number of the large division we need, and then the subdivision. Taking the C scale again as an example and taking the number 1.96, we read 1, the first number on the scale, then go along the scale to the ninth large division between 1 and 2, calling this 9, then to the sixth subdivision between 1.9 and 2 and obtain 1.96. If we desire to read 1.965 we must estimate the 5, half the value of the space between 1.96 and 1.97. This last figure, of course, may be in error as the reading depends on our skill in estimating half the value of a division. 1.967 would be 1.96 and 7/10 the value of a division beyond 1.96, etc.

In reading the slide rule we read only the figures, paying no attention to the decimal point. 1.96, 19.6, 19600, .00196 would all be read the same. The decimal point in computations is located by simple rules given later in this text.

Taking next the space between 2 and 4 on the C scale we find the spaces between 2 to 3 and 3 to 4 each divided into ten large divisions and each large division into five subdivisions. Each subdivision is therefore 2/10. To read 25.6, we read 2, then the fifth large division for the 5 and the third subdivision for the 6, because each subdivision is 2/10, and 3 times 2/10 equals 6/10. If we desire 25.65 we must estimate one-fourth the value of a subdivision, because $\frac{1}{4} \times 2/10 = 1/20 = .05$, and so we have 25.6 + .05 or 25.65.

Between 4 and 10, the main divisions or spaces are each divided into ten large divisions and each large division is divided into two parts. To read 4.55, we first read 4, then the fifth large division for the first 5, and then the first subdivision for the last 5. If we desire 4.56 we must estimate the 6 as 6/10 the value of the space between 4.5 and 4.6.

The same general method of reading the scales applies to the A, B, C, D, and K scales. The CI scale is read the same as the C scale but from the right-hand end of the slide.

The scales for logarithms, sines, and tangents are on the back of the rule; all start at 0 and are read the same as ordinary rules and meters.

USING THE SLIDE RULE

When you become familiar with reading the scales you can quickly learn to multiply, divide, find reciprocals, find square root and cube root and the square and cube of numbers.

If you understand simple trigonometry you can find sines, cosines, tangents, and cotangents on your rule and solve triangles without the use of a book of tables.

By the time you have learned to do the ordinary operations with numbers and work problems involving the use of trigonometry, you will probably want to know the theory of the rule and how to use logarithms. By studying the chapter on "Logarithms and Their Application to the Slide Rule," you will understand the theory of the rule and how to raise numbers to a fractional power like $2^{1.6}$ and to find the fractional root of, say $\sqrt[3.2]{7.5}$.

Proficiency in the use of the rule will come in a very short time by a study of the topics outlined in the pages to follow and by a little practice each day on the problems given.

THE C AND D SCALES

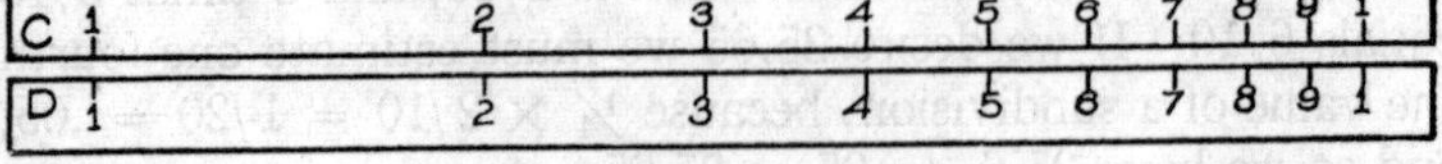

FIG. 2—The C and D Scales of a Slide Rule

These two scales are probably used more than any of the others, for on these multiplication and division are performed.

It is not necessary to go into the theory of the slide rule at this time further than to say that when the 1 on C is set over a number on D, then under any other number on C, there will be found on D, a number that is the sum of the selected numbers on C and D. The operation of setting the scales is similar to setting the end of one foot-rule over a number such as 2 on another foot-rule and under 3 for instance, on the upper rule, reading the sum of 2 and 3 which is 5 on the lower rule. Such a setting is shown by Fig. 3.

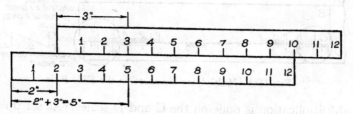

FIG. 3—Two Rules Set for Adding Numbers

The divisions on the C and D scales of the slide rule are not equal, as on ordinary foot-rules, but are proportional to the logarithms of the numbers they represent. It will be explained under "Logarithms and Their Application to the Slide Rule" that when logarithms are added, the numbers they represent are multiplied together.

For the present it is only necessary to remember that to multiply two numbers we set the scales to add together the distances denoted by the numbers printed on them.

CHAPTER II

MULTIPLICATION, DIVISION, AND PROPORTION

SETTING THE SLIDE RULE FOR MULTIPLICATION

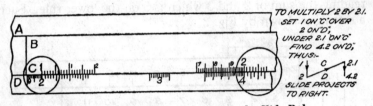

TO MULTIPLY 2 BY 2.1.
SET 1 ON 'C' OVER
2 ON 'D';
UNDER 2.1 ON 'C'
FIND 4.2 ON 'D';
THUS:-

SLIDE PROJECTS
TO RIGHT.

FIG. 4(a)—Multiplying Numbers on the Slide Rule

Multiplication is done on the C and D scales. As set up in Fig. 4(a) the rule multiplies 2 by 2.1. The process is as follows: To multiply two numbers together set 1 on the C scale over one number on the D scale and under the other number on the C scale find the product on the D scale. Thus in Fig 4(a), 1 on C is set over 2 on D; then under 2.1 on C is found 4.2 on D which is the product of 2 and 2.1. With this same setting we could have multiplied 2 by 2.5, 3, 3.5, etc. or any number up to 5 when we should have reached the end of the D scale. If

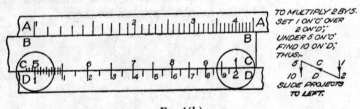

TO MULTIPLY 2 BY 5.
SET 1 ON 'C' OVER
2 ON 'D';
UNDER 5 ON 'C'
FIND 10 ON 'D';
THUS:-

SLIDE PROJECTS
TO LEFT.

FIG. 4(b)

we wanted to multiply 2 by 6 for instance, we would set the 1 at the right-hand end of the C scale over 2 on the D scale with the slide projecting to the left as shown by Fig. 4(b). Then we could multiply 2 by 6, 6.5, 8, 9, etc. up to 10.

To summarize then:

To multiply two numbers set 1 on C over one number on D; then under the other number on C find the product on D.

Practice the following:*

(1) 2.56 × 1.6 =
(2) 2.8 × 3.5 =
(3) 7   × 1.4 =
(4) 9   × 2.1 =

*NOTE: Put your answers in these boxes and then check with those given in the Appendix.

In (4) set the right-hand 1 of C over 9 on D and find 18.9 on D under 2.1 on C.

(5)   6   × 75 =
(6)   3.1 × 4.1 =
(7)   1.8 × 8   =
(8)   .161 × 9   =
(9) 131   × 8   =
(10) 1.15 × 9   =

SETTING THE SLIDE RULE FOR DIVISION

Division is the inverse of multiplication. To divide, find the dividend on D and set the divisor on C directly over it. The quotient will be found on D under the 1 on C. It is best to use the runner to locate the dividend as shown by Fig. 5. In Fig. 5 the rule is set up to divide 26.8 by 2.

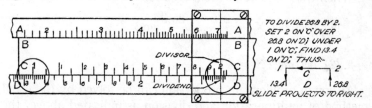

Fig. 5—Slide Rule Set for Dividing

Practice the following:

(1) $\dfrac{6.4}{2} =$ (6) $\dfrac{1080}{8} =$

(2) $\dfrac{940}{3.5} =$ (7) $\dfrac{10.04}{2} =$

(3) $\dfrac{370}{140} =$ (8) $\dfrac{2.01}{52} =$

(4) $\dfrac{225}{13} =$ (9) $\dfrac{4990}{307} =$

(5) $\dfrac{1.68}{12} =$ (10) $\dfrac{0.086}{2} =$

The beginner should remember that in both multiplication and division the D scale is the starting scale. For example: in multiplication, 43×2 is found as (43 on D) $\times$ (2 on C) = 86; in division, $86 \div 2$ is found as (86 on D) $\div$ (2 on C) = 43. Note that in division on the slide rule the divisor is placed over the dividend, whereas in division by arithmetic we are accustomed to set the dividend over the divisor, as a fraction: $\dfrac{86}{2}$.

SETTING THE SLIDE RULE FOR PROPORTION

When the unknown in a proportion is to be found, the proportion is generally written

(1) $\dfrac{X}{210} = \dfrac{26.3}{41.5}$ or   (2) $\dfrac{20.6}{X} = \dfrac{4}{5}$

When these equations are solved for X

(1) becomes $X = \dfrac{210 \times 26.3}{41.5}$ and

(2) becomes $X = \dfrac{5 \times 20.6}{4}$

Although problems in proportion can be solved by the usual method of multiplication and division as indicated above, the slide rule offers a simpler and quicker method. A little study of the rule will show that equations such as (1) and (2) can be set up on the rule *as they stand* and the value of X read off at once.

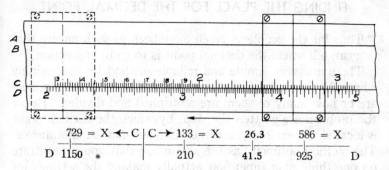

$$729 = X \leftarrow C \mid C \rightarrow 133 = X \qquad 26.3 \qquad 586 = X$$

D 1150 ·   210   41.5   925   D

Fig. 6. Setting the Slide Rule for Proportion

In solving (1) refer to Fig. 6. First find 41.5 on D and set 26.3 on C directly over it. This can best be done by using the runner. If now we want to find what value of X will have the same ratio to 210 as 26.3 has to 41.5, we move the runner to 210 on D and over 210 on D read 133 on C.

If we should want to find X in $\dfrac{X}{925} = \dfrac{26.3}{41.5}$

we let the slide remain as it was with 26.3 on C over 41.5 on D and simply move the runner to 925 on D. Under the hairline of the runner we find 586 on C.

To find X in $\dfrac{X}{1150} = \dfrac{26.3}{41.5}$ move the slide so that the right-

hand index of C stands where the left-hand index stood, that is, at 158 on D, and over 1150 on D read 729 on C.

In (2): Over 5 on D set 4 on C.

         Under 20.6 on C read 25.7 on D.

Note that in the above solutions of ratios the figures are set up on the rule as they stand on the page. That is, 26.3 is over 41.5 and X is over 210, 925, and 1150. This setting is the inverse of regular division but is one of the time-saving schemes that the slide rule offers.

CHAPTER III

FINDING THE PLACE FOR THE DECIMAL POINT

Thus far the problems given have been of such nature that one can tell where the decimal point is to go by inspection.

There is a very simple and reliable method for determining where the decimal point is to go, no matter what the numbers are or how many of them are multiplied and divided. Below the problem are written the steps by which the decimal point is located. Therefore you can check your method and answer. The method outlined has the advantage that you concentrate on one thing at a time: first actually making the settings for multiplying and dividing, and then, as a second entirely separate operation, finding where to put the decimal point.

A number such as 352 is made up of 3 figures usually called "digits." While this name for the figures of a whole number is all right, it does not describe the zeros in a number such as 0.00352. In this book the word *SPAN* will be used to describe the number of digits making up a whole number, and with a negative sign the number of zeros before the first significant figure in a decimal fraction. The following will illustrate the use of the word span:

Number	Span		Number	Span
352.	3		0.0352	−1
35.2	2		0.00352	−2
3.52	1		0.000352	−3
0.352	0		0.0000352	−4

RIGHT AND LEFT PROJECTIONS OF THE SLIDE

In practicing with the slide rule on the problems of pages 9 and 10 it was seen that the slide sometimes projected to the right and sometimes to the left. A study of many settings of the rule has revealed the fact that these right-hand and left-hand projections of the slide can be made use of in determining the position of the decimal point in multiplication and division. The method of using the projections is as follows:

1. When the slide projects to the left.
   - (a) In multiplying, add the spans of the numbers multiplied together to find the span of the product.
   - (b) In dividing, subtract the spans of the numbers in the divisor from span or sum of the spans in the dividend.

2. When the slide projects to the right.
   - (a) In multiplying, add the spans of the numbers multiplied together but subtract 1 for every right-hand projection of the slide.
   - (b) In dividing, subtract the spans of the numbers in the divisor from the span or sum of the spans in the dividend, but add 1 for each right-hand projection of the slide.

In order that we shall not forget this simple method of locating the decimal point, it is a good plan to express it in formulas and mark these formulas on the upper left-hand and right-hand corners of your rule as in Fig. 6.

$$\times = \text{SUM} \qquad\qquad \times = \text{SUM} \quad -1$$
$$\div = \text{DIFF.} \qquad\qquad \div = \text{DIFF.} \quad +1$$

This marking is clearly shown by Fig. 7.

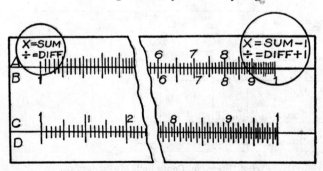

Fig. 7. Rule Marked with Formulas for Finding Position of Decimal Point

LOCATING THE DECIMAL POINT WHEN MULTIPLYING

We will first take an example where the slide always projects to the left.

$$3.5 \times 76 \times 0.00795 \times 8200$$

First multiply the numbers together as shown by Fig. 8, proceeding as follows:

Step 1. Set right-hand 1 on C over 3.5 on D. Under 76 on C read 266 on D. 266 is the product of 3.5×76 when the decimal point is not considered. Move the runner to 266 on D.

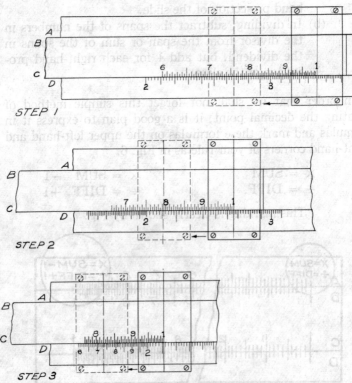

Fig. 8. Steps in Continued Multiplication

Step 2.   With the runner at 266 on D, bring the right-hand 1 on C to the hairline of the runner and under 795 on C read 211 on D. 211 is the product of 266 and 795 when the decimal point is not considered. Move the runner to 211 on D.

Step 3.   With the runner at 211 on D, bring right-hand 1 on C to the hairline of the runner and under 82 on C read 1734 on D. 1734 is the product of 211 and 82 when the decimal point is not considered.

In this problem as the slide always projects to the left, the span of the product is the sum of the spans of the separate factors. To prevent error in summarizing the spans, write down the spans, tying all the plus values together at the top and the minus values at the bottom, and then subtract. The separate spans and their total for this problem will then be:

$$1 + 2 + -2 + 4 = \begin{array}{r} 7 \\ -2 \\ \hline 5 \end{array}$$

The span of the product will be 5 and as the figures are 1734 the correct answer will be 17340.

Next, take a problem where the slide projects to the right. In multiplying for every right projection we must subtract 1. Therefore, we must keep track of *all right projections*, and mark a small capital "R" by the number that made the slide project to the right. *Do this while you are making your settings.* With some practice you will do this with little effort.

The following problem will illustrate the method used:

(1) $22 \times 144^R \times 0.00198^R \times 1300^R = 8150$

(2) $2 + 3 + -2 + 4 \, -3 = \begin{array}{r} 9 \\ -5 \\ \hline 4 \end{array}$

In the above we found that the figures were 815. Adding the spans and subtracting 3 for 3 right projections we obtain a span of 4 or the product is 8150.

Practice the following:

(1) $14.6 \times 90 \times 0.0000025^R \times 2960^R = 9.72$

$$2 + 2 + -5 + 4 + -2 = \quad 8$$
$$\frac{-7}{1}$$

(Solution at left is for Problem 1, p. 15.)

(2) $14.5 \times 26 \times 0.00002 \times 1260 \ = $

(3) $2.55 \times 3.1416 \times 108 \ = $

(4) $0.00195 \times 195 \times 350 \ = $

(5) $2090 \times 0.0032 \times 1045 \times 0.096 \ = $

LOCATING THE DECIMAL POINT WHEN DIVIDING

When the slide projects to the left: subtract the span of the divisor from the span of the dividend, thus,

$$\frac{425}{72} = 5.9 \qquad\qquad \left(\begin{array}{l} 425 = 3 \text{ span} \\ 72 = 2 \text{ span} \end{array} \right)$$

($\div$ = Diff.) $3 - 2 = 1$, that is, the quotient has a span of 1. The number is therefore 5.9.

When the slide projects to the right: subtract the span of the divisor from the span of the dividend but add 1 for every right-hand projection, thus,

$$\frac{425}{19.5_{R}} = 21.8$$

19.5 made the slide project to the right; so we write a small "R" below and to the right of 19.5; then from ($\div$ = Diff. + 1),

$3 - 2 + 1 = 4$ which means that the quotient has a span of 2 or
$$\frac{-2}{2} \qquad \text{is } 21.8.$$

Practice the following:

(1) $\dfrac{45.3}{71} \ = $

$2 - 2 \ = \quad 0$

(2) $\dfrac{7400}{41.5_{R}} \ = $

$4 - 2 + 1 = 5$
$$\frac{-2}{3}$$

(3) $\dfrac{0.00275}{85} \ = $

$-2 \ -2 \quad = \quad -4$

(4) $\dfrac{27}{0.0155_{R}} \ = $

$2 - - 1 + 1 = 2 \oplus 1 + 1 = 4$

(5) $\dfrac{755}{0.0272_R} =$ ☐

$3- \; -1 + 1 = 3 \oplus 1 + 1 = 5$

Minus -1 is equal to $+1$. The symbol $\oplus$ is used to show that $- \; -1$ has been changed to plus 1 and to avoid reading the change to $+1$ as $-1 \; -1$ which is sometimes done if the ordinary symbol is carelessly made.

MULTIPLICATION AND DIVISION COMBINED

In fractions like

$$\frac{6.2 \times 192}{14 \times 0.0225}$$

the correct way to solve is by dividing and multiplying "crisscross." That is, divide 6.2 by 14, then multiply this answer by 192, and finally divide by 0.0225. Note in each operation whether the slide projects to the right. If it does put an "R" by the number that made it project to the right. Put the "R" above and to the right of the number if in the numerator, and below and to the right of the number if in the denominator. Total the spans in the same "crisscross" order that you used in dividing and multiplying. Fig. 9 shows the procedure for the problem given.

Step 1. Bring the hairline of the runner to 6.2 on D and set 14 on C to the hairline. Under 1 on C find 443 on D. 443 is 6.2 divided by 14 when the position of the decimal point is not considered. Note that the slide projects to the right and mark "R" immediately as shown on page 18.

Step 2. With 1 on C still at 443 on D, move the hairline on the runner to 192 on C and under it read 85 on D. Note that the slide projects to the right and mark "R" immediately as shown.

Step 3. With the hairline of the runner at 85 on D, bring 0.0225 on C to the hairline and under 1 on C read 378 on D.

378 is the final answer when the position of the decimal point is not considered. Move the hairline of the runner to 378 on D to complete the solution and mark "R" as shown. The complete solution of the problem will appear on your paper as follows:

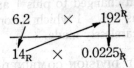

Fig. 9 shows the positions of the runner.

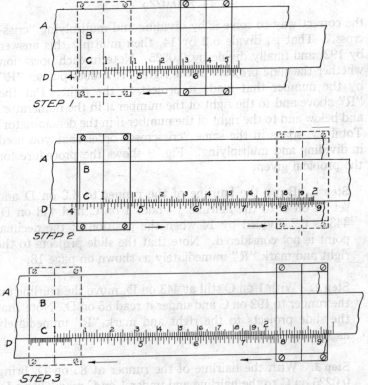

Fig. 9. Steps in Multiplication and Division Combined

The spans will be

$$1 - 2 + 3 - -1 + 1$$

or $\quad 1 - 2 + 3 \oplus 1 + 1 = \begin{array}{r} 6 \\ -2 \\ \hline 4 \end{array}$

and since the figures in the answer are 378, the correct answer is 3780. Note that an "R" in the numerator may be cancelled with an "R" in the denominator.

Practice the following:

(1) $\dfrac{42 \times 45.5}{5 \times 0.0695} = $ ⬚

$2 - 1 + 2 \oplus 1 = \begin{array}{r} 5 \\ -1 \\ \hline 4 \end{array}$

(2) $\dfrac{362 \times 0.0052}{25 \times 0.081} = $

(3) $\dfrac{0.00826 \times 35}{71.5 \times 0.022} = $

(4) $\dfrac{0.0074 \times 76}{0.81} = $

(5) $\dfrac{2 \times 8 \times 16}{4 \times 32 \times 64} = $

(6) $\dfrac{25 \times 32.8 \times 0.0075}{22 \times 0.06 \times 0.008} = $

(7) $\dfrac{260}{437 \times 0.00362} = $

In problem (7) note that since the quantity 0.00362 is in the denominator you must divide by it.

(8) $\dfrac{44 \times 0.002 \times 0.06}{22 \times 0.04 \times 24} = $

(9) $\dfrac{143.5 \times 2.3 \times 2}{82 \times 56} = $

(10) $\dfrac{160 \times 52 \times 0.00092}{92.8 \times 40 \times 0.081} = $

LOCATING THE DECIMAL POINT IN SPECIAL CASES

When the same product may be obtained with the slide projecting either to the left or the right, use the left-hand projection in finding the place for the decimal point.

Example: $2 \times 5 = 10$. This product may be found with either the right-hand or left-hand 1 on C set opposite 2 on D. Only the left-hand projection will give the correct location of the decimal point. With a left-hand projection, the product is found thus: $2 \times 5 = 10$ $1 + 1 = 2$, that is, span is 2.

Example: $4 \times 25 = 100$. Either a left-hand or right-hand projection will bring the 1 on C opposite 25 on D, but only a left-hand projection will give the correct location of the decimal point. With a left-hand projection, the solution is as follows: $4 \times 25 = 100$ $1 + 2 = 3$ (span is 3).

When the rule closes up in making computations, call the setting that makes the rule close up a right-hand projection.

Example: $2 \times 40 \times \frac{1}{8} = 10$. In dividing 2 times 40 by 8, the operation of dividing by 8 causes the rule to close up, forming a *right-hand projection*. The solution is: $2 \times 40^\mathbf{R} \times \frac{1}{8}\mathbf{R} = 10$

$$1 + 2 - 1 = +3$$
$$\frac{-1}{+2} \text{ (span is 2)}$$

Example: $\dfrac{2 \times 6}{4 \times 30} = 0.1$. Working criss-cross as usual, 2 divided by 4 and multiplied by 6 all give left-hand projections. The operation of dividing by 30 causes the rule to close up, making a right-hand projection. The problem would then be set down as follows:

$$\left(\frac{2 \times 6}{4 \times 30_\mathbf{R}}\right) = 0.1 \qquad 1 - 1 + 1 - 2 + 1 = +3$$
$$\frac{-3}{0}$$

that is, the decimal point is just before the 1.

When a power of 10, such as 10, 100, 1000, etc., appears alone, solve the problem as usual but neglect the power of 10 on the slide rule. After obtaining the proper answer without the power of 10, move the decimal point to the right or left as many places as there are cyphers in the power of 10. Move to the right if multiplying by a power of 10 and to the left if dividing by a power of 10.

Example: $2 \times 8.5 \times 1,000 = 17,000$

First, $2 \times 8.5 = 17$; then, 17 times 1,000 = 17,000

Example: $\dfrac{4.5 \times 3}{.006 \times 1,000} = 2.25$

First, $\left(\dfrac{4.5 \times 3}{.006}\right) = 2250$

$$1 - - 2 + 1$$
$$= 1 \oplus 2 + 1 = 4 \text{ (span is 4)}$$

then, 2250 divided by 1,000 equals 2.25

When a power of 10 does not appear alone, as in say, 37,500, make the computations in the usual way.

Example: $\dfrac{5 \times 3}{2 \times 37,500} = .0002$

$$1 - 1 + 1 - 5 + 1 = +3$$
$$-6$$
$$\overline{-3} \text{ (3 cyphers after decimal point)}$$

CHAPTER IV

CI SCALE AND FOLDED SCALES CF AND DF

The CI scale is found on the slide between the B and C scales: CI means "C inverted." The divisions on the CI scale are the same size as those on the C scale but they are engraved on the slide to read in the opposite direction, that is, from right to left instead of from left to right.

The CI scale is used:

1. To find the reciprocal of a number or the value of 1 divided by the number.
2. To speed up multiplication and division.

THE CI SCALE USED TO FIND RECIPROCALS

When the slide is pushed in until the 1's on the slide match the 1's on the rule, any number on the CI scale is the reciprocal of the number directly below it on the C scale. For instance in Fig. 10, 0.5 on the CI scale is the reciprocal of 2 which is below it on the C scale; 0.333 on the CI scale is the reciprocal of 3 which is below it on the C scale.

TO FIND ½. OVER 2 ON C FIND 0.5 ON CI

Fig. 10. The CI Scale Used to Find Reciprocals

The following method may be used to find the position of the decimal point in a reciprocal when the position is not easily determined by inspection.

When the given number is an integer, that is, a whole number like 25 or 2600, or a mixed number which consists of a whole number and fraction like 7.83 or 1.08, the reciprocal will be a decimal fraction. The first significant figure of the decimal fraction will stand as many places from the decimal point as there are digits in the whole number, or to use the notation of this book, the first significant figure of the reciprocal will stand as many places from the decimal point as the span of the given number. By significant figures is meant the figures remaining in a whole number or decimal after the zeros at the right or left have been removed. Thus the significant figures in 25000 or 0.00025 are in each case 25.

Examples:

$$\text{Reciprocal of } 368 = 0.0\overset{1\ 2\ 3}{0}272; \quad \text{Span} = 3, \text{ first figure} \\ \text{3rd place}$$

$$52 = 0.\overset{1\ 2}{0}1923; \quad \text{Span} = 2, \text{ first figure} \\ \text{2nd place}$$

$$5 = 0.\overset{1}{2} \quad ; \quad \text{Span} = 1, \text{ first figure} \\ \text{1st place}$$

When the given number is a decimal fraction, the reciprocal will be an integer or mixed number. The span of the reciprocal will be the same as the number of the place that the first significant figure of the given number stands from the decimal point.

Examples:

Reciprocal of

$$0.5 = 2 \qquad \text{1st place, span} = 1$$
$$0.56 = 1.786 \qquad \text{1st place, span} = 1$$
$$0.0\overset{1\ 2\ 3}{0}62 = 161.3 \qquad \text{3rd place, span} = 3$$
$$0.0\overset{1\ 2\ 3\ 4\ 5}{0}00873 = 11450 \qquad \text{5th place, span} = 5$$

Verify the following:

Reciprocal of

$$256 = 0.0\overset{1\ 2\ 3}{0}391 \qquad \text{Span} = 3, \text{ first figure 3rd place}$$
$$29.2 = 0.0342$$
$$7.6 = 0.132$$
$$760 = 0.00132$$
$$1075 = 0.00093$$
$$28000 = 0.0000357$$
$$0.51 = 1.96 \qquad \text{1st place, span} = 1$$
$$0.872 = 1.147$$
$$0.0932 = 10.73$$
$$0.000183 = 5460$$
$$0.009500 = 105.3$$
$$0.000060 = 16670$$

THE CI SCALE USED TO SPEED UP MULTIPLICATION AND DIVISION

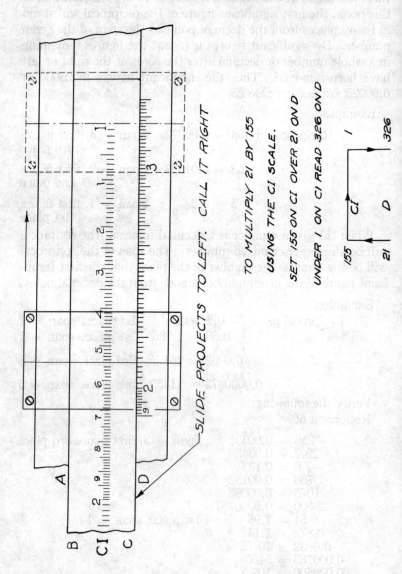

Fig. 11. The CI Scale Used for Multiplication

Fig. 11 shows how to use the CI scale in multiplying 21 by 155. First bring the hairline of the runner to 21 on D and then set 155 on CI over 21 on D. Under 1 on CI read 326 on D. Since CI is an inverted scale this setting multiplies 21 by 155. The slide projects to the left and so we must call it "right." We then have

$$21 \times 155^R = 3260$$

$$2 + 3 - 1 = 5$$
$$ \; \underline{-1}$$
$$ \; 4$$

Fig. 12 shows how to divide 270 by 5 using the CI scale. First bring the hairline of the runner to 270 on D and set left-hand 1 on CI over 270 on D. Under 5 on CI read 54 on D. Since CI is an inverted scale this setting divides 270 by 5. The slide projects to the right and so we must call it "left." We then have

$$\frac{270}{5} = 54$$

$$3 - 1 = 2$$

Multiplication and division can often be speeded up by using the CI scale because numbers needed on the C scale may require that the slide be moved nearly its whole length to multiply or divide, whereas if the CI scale is used the numbers needed can often be found on the CI scale by moving the slide only a little. For instance, supposing during multiplication and division we found 10 on C over 9 on D and the next step is to multiply by 105. If we use the C scale we would move the slide to the right its whole length so that 1 on C would stand over 9 on D. Then under 105 on C we would read 945 on D. If we use the CI scale, 105 on CI is only about a quarter of an inch from 10 on C. So we move the slide to the right until 105 on CI stands over 9 on D and under 1 on C read 945 on D.

Summarizing: Because of the "inverted" scale, multiplication on CI is like division on C, division on CI like multiplication on C. Right projections are "left." Left projections are

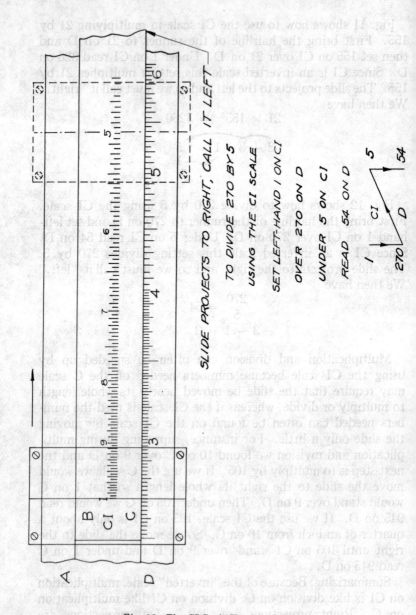

SLIDE PROJECTS TO RIGHT, CALL IT LEFT

TO DIVIDE 270 BY 5

USING THE CI SCALE

SET LEFT-HAND I ON CI

OVER 270 ON D

UNDER 5 ON CI

READ 54 ON D

Fig. 12. The CI Scale Used for Division

"right." In continued multiplication and division watch the CI scale and when a needed number comes up that requires but little movement of the slide, and the same number using the C scale requires a large movement of the slide, use the CI scale.

Combined division and multiplication by the CI and C scales: Use as an example,

$$\frac{752 \times 91}{36 \times 52}$$

Divide 752 by 36 using the C scale in the usual way and obtain 20.9. Note that the slide projects to the right and mark a small "R" below and to the right of 36. Now move the slide slightly to the left until 91 on the CI scale stands over 20.9. Under 1 on CI you will find 1902 on the D scale which is the product of 20.9 and 91. Note that the slide projects to the right which is the equivalent of to the left on C. Finally divide 1902 by 52 using the CI scale as you would the C scale for multiplication and obtain 36.6. Note that the slide projects to the right and as you are using the CI scale call it "left."

The operations are pictured below:

$$\underset{\text{C}}{\underbrace{\frac{752 \times 91}{36_{\text{R}} \times 52}}} = 36.6$$

$$3 - 2 + 2 - 2 + 1 = 6$$
$$\frac{-4}{2}$$

Practice the following using the C and CI scales:

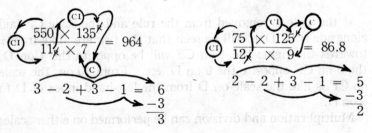

$$\frac{550 \times 135}{11 \times 7} = 964$$

$$3 - 2 + 3 - 1 = 6$$
$$\frac{-3}{3}$$

$$\frac{75 \times 125}{12 \times 9} = 86.8$$

$$2 - 2 + 3 - 1 = 5$$
$$\frac{-3}{2}$$

FOLDED SCALES CF AND DF

The folded scales along the upper edge of certain slide rules, such as the Keuffel and Esser Doric No. 4168 (shown in Fig. 13), make it possible to perform computations with fewer settings of the slide than is otherwise possible. Further, since the folded scales start and end with π (3.1416), computations involving π can be made very quickly.

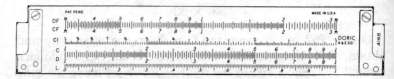

Fig. 13.   Keuffel and Esser Doric No. 4168.

The lettering CF and DF on the scales means "C folded" and "D folded." The term "folded" can be understood by the sketch Fig. 14. A section of the rule is folded to the left until its left-hand end is directly over the 1's (indexes) on the C and D scales. CF and DF are thus scales C and D extended.

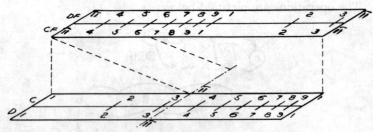

Fig. 14.   Sketch Showing How a Part of the C and D Scale Is Folded Back to Make the CF and DF Scales.

If the slide is removed from the rule and the scale CF laid alongside scale D, it will be seen that the two are alike from π towards the right: the 4 on CF will be opposite the 4 on D, the 9 on CF opposite the 9 on D, etc. From 10 on, the scale on CF is like the scale on D from the left-hand index of D to π on D.

Multiplication and division can be performed on either scales

C and D or scales CF and DF. For example, to multiply 5.5 by 6 on the C and D scales, set 1 on C opposite 5.5 on D; then opposite 6 on C find the product 33 on D. To multiply 5.5 by 6 on the CF and DF scales, set 1 on CF opposite 5.5 on DF; then opposite 6 on CF read 33 on DF. In dividing 84 by 21

$$\frac{84 \text{ (on D)}}{21 \text{ (on C)}} = 4 \text{ (on D)} \quad \text{and} \quad \frac{84 \text{ (on DF)}}{21 \text{ (on CF)}} = 4 \text{ (on DF)}$$

Since the scales are identical but placed in different positions on the rule, fewer settings are needed in making computations. For example, suppose that 3 is to be multiplied by 4, that the C and D scales are used and a right-hand extension is tried for this product. When 1 on C is set opposite 3 on D, it will be noticed at once that 4 is beyond the right-hand end of D and that the slide must be pushed to the left until the 1 at the right-hand end of C stands over 3 on D. The answer 12 will then be found on D opposite 4 on C. If, instead of moving the slide to the left to find the product of 3 and 4, one looks to 4 on CF, he will find 12 on DF without another setting.

To find the position of the decimal point in multiplication when using the CF and DF scales, notice whether the regular C scale extends to the right or the left when reading the product on DF. If it extends to the *right* and you have to use CF and DF to get your answer, call the CF extension *left*. If scale C extends to the *left* and you have to use CF and DF to get your answer, call the extension *right*.

Example: Using the preceding example of 3 × 4 = 12 and a right-hand extension of C, 4 on C extends beyond the end of D, so C would have to be pushed to the left to get the right-hand index of C opposite 3 on D in order to obtain the answer 12. As the CF and DF scales enable you to obtain this answer without a left-hand extension of C, call the CF extension *left*.

Example: 2.5 × 2 = 5. If we use the C and D scales and a left-hand extension, 2.5 is beyond the left-hand end of D and we would need to push the slide to the right so that 1 on C would stand opposite 2.5 on D to obtain the product 5. With the left-hand extension on D we can read 5 directly on DF opposite 2 on CF, so we call CF a *right-hand* extension.

CHAPTER V

SLIDE RULE OPERATIONS INVOLVING SQUARES AND SQUARE ROOTS

SQUARING A NUMBER

The numbers on the A scale are the squares of the numbers on the D scale. Hence to find the square of a number bring the hairline of the runner to the number on the D scale and find the square of the number under the hairline on the A scale. Fig. 15 shows how to find the square of 2.5.

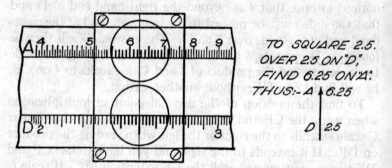

TO SQUARE 2.5.
OVER 2.5 ON "D,"
FIND 6.25 ON "A":
THUS:- A ↑ 6.25

D 2.5

Fig. 15. Finding the Square of a Number

Examples:

$$3.5^2 = 12.25$$
$$4.2^2 = 17.64$$
$$10.4^2 = 108.2$$

FINDING THE POSITION OF THE DECIMAL POINT IN SQUARING NUMBERS

Examination of the A scale will show it to be divided into two sections. The first or left section is divided from 0 to 10 and the second or right section is divided from 10 to 100. Mark the first section of your rule 2S − 1 and the second section 2S as shown by Fig. 16.

30

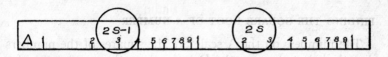

Fig. 16. How to Mark the First and Second Sections of Scale A

S stands for "Span" which was explained under "Multiplication and Division."

In squaring, if the square of the number on the D scale is found on the first section of the A scale, its span is $2S - 1$. If the square of the number is found in the second section of the A scale, its span is $2S$.

The following examples will illustrate:

$2.5^2 = 6.25$
  1st section of A scale, $S = 1$, $2S - 1 = 2 \times 1 - 1 = 1$

$2550^2 = 6,500,000$
  1st section of A scale, $S = 4$, $2S - 1 = 2 \times 4 - 1 = 7$

$0.0027^2 = 0.0000073$
  1st section of A scale, $S = -2$, $2S - 1 = 2 \times (-2) - 1 = -5$

$6^2 = 36$
  2nd section of A scale, $S = 1$, $2S = 2 \times 1 = 2$

$41^2 = 1681$
  2nd section of A scale, $S = 2$, $2S = 2 \times 2 = 4$

$0.062^2 = 0.00384$
  2nd section of A scale, $S = -1$, $2S = 2 \times (-1) = -2$

$0.48^2 = 0.2304$
  2nd section of A scale, $S = 0$, $2S = 2 \times 0 = 0$

Explain the following:

$$26^2 = 676$$
$$0.086^2 = 0.0074$$
$$5642^2 = 31,830,000$$
$$0.0028^2 = 0.00000784$$
$$28938^2 = 837,000,000$$

FINDING THE SQUARE ROOT OF A NUMBER

The numbers on the A scale are the squares of the numbers directly below them on the D scale; thus, the square root of a number may be found by bringing the hairline of the runner to the number on the A scale and finding the square root of the number under the hairline on the D scale. Fig. 17 shows how to find the square root of 9.3.

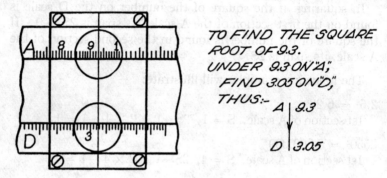

TO FIND THE SQUARE
ROOT OF 9.3.
UNDER 9.3 ON "A",
FIND 3.05 ON "D",
THUS:-

A | 9.3
↓
D | 3.05

Fig. 17. Finding the Square Root of a Number

FINDING THE POSITION OF THE DECIMAL POINT IN THE SQUARE ROOT OF A WHOLE OR MIXED NUMBER

It was explained in the squaring of numbers that the A scale is divided into two sections: the section at the left-hand end of the rule starting at 1 and going to 10 at the center of the rule, and the section at the right-hand end of the rule starting at 10 at the center of the rule and going to 100 at the right-hand end of the rule. It was further explained that the squares of numbers on the D scale are found on the A scale. Numbers on the D scale are therefore the square roots of numbers on the A scale. It only remains, then, to decide which section of the A scale to use in finding the square roots of whole numbers like 2963 or 285 and mixed numbers like 378.635.

The method used in arithmetic can be used equally well with the slide rule. That is: divide the number into "periods" of two figures each, beginning at the decimal point. For example in 2963 the decimal point though not written down is understood to follow the 3, in 285 to follow the 5, etc. So 2963 would be divided thus: 29̑63, giving two whole "periods." 285 would be divided 2̑85, giving one whole period and one partial period. 378.635 would be divided thus: 3̑78.6̑35̑0, giving one whole period and one partial period to the left of the decimal point and two whole periods to the right of the decimal point.

From the above method of dividing the number into periods we find the proper section of the A scale to use. The method is as follows. 29̑63 means we use the part of the A scale that gives us 29, namely the right-hand section (10 to 100). 2̑85 means we use the section of the A scale that gives us 2, which is the left-hand section (1 to 10). 3̑78.6̑35̑0 means we use the left-hand section that gives us 3 (1 to 10).

Summarizing:

$$\sqrt{29̑63} \quad = 54.4$$

$$\sqrt{2̑85} \quad = 16.88$$

$$\sqrt{3̑78.6̑35̑0} = 19.46$$

Examples:

(1) $\sqrt{28̑53}$ = [ ]   (2) $\sqrt{3̑75̑60}$ = [ ]

(3) $\sqrt{4.5̑3}$ = [ ]   (4) $\sqrt{1̑62̑87̑0}$ = [ ]

FINDING THE POSITION OF THE DECIMAL POINT IN THE SQUARE ROOT OF A DECIMAL FRACTION

Divide the decimal fraction into periods of two figures each beginning at the decimal point. If the last period to the right contains but one figure, make it a complete period by annexing a zero. There will be as many zeros between the decimal point and first digit in the square root as there are whole zero periods between the decimal point and the first period having digits in the original number. Thus:

$\sqrt{0.\overline{00}\ \overline{00}\ \overline{25}}$ Two whole zero periods in given number

$= 0.0\ \ 0\ \ 5$ Two zeros in square root

$\sqrt{0.\overline{00}\ \overline{00}\ \overline{05}}$ Two whole zero periods in given number

$= 0.0\ \ 0\ \ 224$ Two zeros in square root

$\sqrt{0.\overline{05}}$ No whole zero periods in given number

$= 0.224$ No zero period in square root

$\sqrt{0.005} = \sqrt{0.00\overline{50}}$ One whole zero period in given number

$= 0.0\,71$ One zero in square root

Explain the following:

$\sqrt{0.0028}\ \ \ \ = 0.0529$ $\qquad$ $\sqrt{0.4930}\ \ \ = 0.702$

$\sqrt{0.000395} = 0.01987$ $\qquad$ $\sqrt{0.08}\ \ \ \ \ \ = 0.283$

$\sqrt{0.0060}\ \ \ \ = 0.0775$ $\qquad$ $\sqrt{0.00715} = 0.0846$

K

CHAPTER VI

SLIDE RULE OPERATIONS INVOLVING CUBES AND CUBE ROOTS

CUBING A NUMBER ON SLIDE RULES HAVING A K SCALE

The K scale contains the cubes of numbers found on the D scale. It is easy to remember this scale, thus: "KUBE." The K scale is divided into three sections known as the first, second, and third section. The first section goes from 0 to 10, the second section 10 to 100, and the third section 100 to 1000. To find the cube of a number bring the hairline of the runner to the number on the D scale and find the cube of the number on the K scale.

Fig. 18 shows how to find the cube of 2.1.

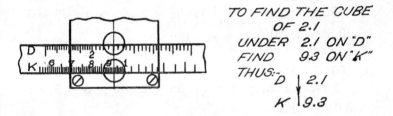

TO FIND THE CUBE
OF 2.1
UNDER 2.1 ON "D"
FIND 9.3 ON "K"
THUS:—

| D | 2.1 |
| K | 9.3 |

Fig. 18. Finding the Cube of a Number on the K Scale

Examples:

$$1.55^3 = 3.72$$
$$3.5^3 = 42.9$$
$$6.9^3 = 328$$

FINDING THE POSITION OF THE DECIMAL POINT IN CUBING NUMBERS

Mark the first section of the K scale $3S-2$, the second section $3S-1$, and the third section $3S$ as shown in Fig. 19.

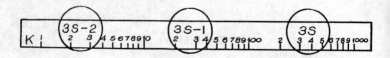

Fig. 19. How to Mark the Three Sections of the K Scale

With the rule marked as in Fig. 19 find the number to be cubed on the D scale and bring the hairline of the runner to this number. The cube of the number will be on the K scale. Note whether it is in the section marked $3S-2$, $3S-1$, or $3S$. Determine the position of the decimal point by substitution in the formula you have marked on the rule. For instance, the figures for the cube of 3.2 are 33 and they are found in the second section of the K scale. The cube has therefore $3S-1$ or $3 \times 1 - 1 = 2$ figures to the left of the decimal point and the number is 33.

The following examples will illustrate the method:

$2.1^3 = 9.26$
First section, $S = 1$, $3S - 2 = 3 \times 1 - 2 = 1$

$13.5^3 = 2,460$
First section, $S = 2$, $3S - 2 = 3 \times 2 - 2 = 4$

$190^3 = 6,860,000$
First section, $S = 3$, $3S - 2 = 3 \times 3 - 2 = 7$

$3.04^3 = 28.1$
Second section, $S = 1$, $3S - 1 = 3 \times 1 - 1 = 2$

$43^3 = 79,500$
Second section, $S = 2$, $3S - 1 = 3 \times 2 - 1 = 5$

$450^3 = 91,100,000$
Second section, $S = 3$, $3S - 1 = 3 \times 3 - 1 = 8$

$5.1^3 = 132.7$
Third section, $S = 1$, $3S = 3$

$77.5^3 = 465,000$
Third section, $S = 2$, $3S = 6$

$952^3 = 863,000,000$
Third section, $S = 3$, $3S = 9$

FINDING THE CUBE ROOT OF A NUMBER USING THE K SCALE

The numbers on the K scale are the cubes of the numbers on the D scale. The cube root of a number may be found by bringing the hairline of the runner to the number on the K scale and finding the cube root of the number under the hairline on the D scale.

Fig. 20 shows how to find the cube root of 28.5.

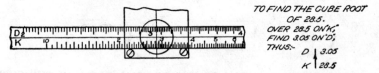

Fig. 20. Finding the Cube Root of a Number by Using the K Scale

FINDING THE POSITION OF THE DECIMAL POINT IN THE CUBE ROOT OF A WHOLE OR MIXED NUMBER

The D and K scales are used in finding the cube roots of numbers. As explained, K stands for "KUBE," and numbers on the K scale are the cubes of numbers on the D scale.

The K scale is divided into three sections. The left-hand section begins at 1 and ends at 10; the center section begins at 10 and ends at 100; the right-hand section begins at 100 and ends at 1000. The procedure in selecting the proper section of the K scale is similar to that in selecting the proper section of the A scale in square root; but in cube root the whole or mixed number is divided into periods of *three figures* each beginning at the decimal point. Thus:

Given Number		Section of K Used	Cube Root Found on D Scale
8000 is divided	8000	Left-hand (1 to 10)	20
25350 "	25350	Center (10 to 100)	29.4
650275 "	650275	Right-hand (100 to 1000)	86.6
9.5 "	9.500	Left-hand (1 to 10)	2.12
26.005 "	26.005	Center (10 to 100)	2.96
853.02 "	853.020	Right-hand (100 to 1000)	9.48

Examples:

(1) $\sqrt[3]{151000} =$ ⬚

(4) $\sqrt[3]{15280} =$ ⬚

(2) $\sqrt[3]{4760} =$ ⬚

(5) $\sqrt[3]{80.260} =$ ⬚

(3) $\sqrt[3]{569} =$ ⬚

(6) $\sqrt[3]{7.6} =$ ⬚

FINDING THE POSITION OF THE DECIMAL POINT IN THE CUBE ROOT OF A DECIMAL FRACTION

Divide the decimal fraction into periods of three figures each beginning at the decimal point. If the last period to the right is not a whole three-figure period, make it one by annexing zeros. There will be as many zeros between the decimal point and the first digit in the cube root as there are whole zero periods between the decimal point and the first period having digits in the original number. Thus:

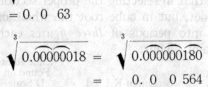

$\sqrt[3]{0.000253}$
$= 0.\ 0\ 63$

One whole zero period in given number
One zero in cube root

$\sqrt[3]{0.00000018} = \sqrt[3]{0.000000180}$
$=\ \ 0.\ 0\ \ 0\ 564$

Two whole zero periods in given number
Two zeros in cube root

$\sqrt[3]{0.00005} = \sqrt[3]{0.000050}$
$=\ 0.\ 0\ 368$

One whole zero period in given number
One zero in cube root

$\sqrt[3]{0.002}$
$= 0.126$

No whole zero periods in given number
No zeros in cube root

FINDING THE CUBE ROOT OF A NUMBER ON A RULE THAT DOES NOT HAVE A K SCALE

Refer to Fig. 21. On the A scale find the given number whose cube root is to be obtained. Slide the B scale along the A scale and watch the numbers on the B scale as they pass under the given number. At the same time watch the numbers on the D scale that the 1 on the C scale passes over. When a number on the B scale under the given number matches a number on the D scale under 1 on the C scale, that number is the cube root of the given number. For instance take 8 on the A scale. Slide B past 8 until 2 on B comes under 8 on A. Then under 1 on C, 2 will be found on D. 2 is the cube root of 8. Fig. 16 shows the setting to obtain the cube root of 4. 1.59 on B under 4 on A matches 1.59 on D under 1 on C, so 1.59 is the cube root of 4.

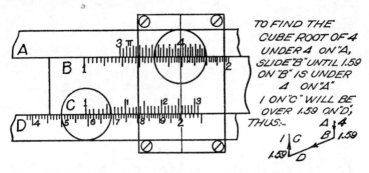

Fig. 21. Finding the Cube Root of a Number on a Rule That Does Not Have a K Scale

CUBING A NUMBER ON A RULE THAT DOES NOT HAVE A K SCALE

As explained under "Squaring a Number," numbers on the A scale are the squares of the numbers on the D scale. Further examination of the A scale shows that it could be used with the B scale for multiplication just as the C and D scales can be used, except that the numbers obtained by multiplying two numbers together on the A and B scales will be the squares of the numbers on the C and D scales. Hence, if we multiply a number by itself using the C, D, B, and A scales instead of the C and D scales we will obtain the cube of the number. This is shown by Fig. 22 where the rule is set up to obtain the cube of 2.1.

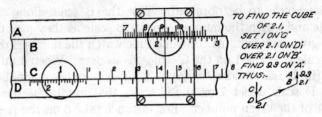

TO FIND THE CUBE
OF 2.1,
SET I ON 'C'
OVER 2.1 ON'D'
OVER 2.1 ON 'B'
FIND 9.3 ON 'A'.
THUS:-

Fig. 22. Cubing a Number by Using the C and D and A and B Scales

CHAPTER VII

SLIDE RULE OPERATIONS INVOLVING THE COMMON TRIGONOMETRIC FUNCTIONS

THE COMMON TRIGONOMETRIC FUNCTIONS

The slide rule may be used to obtain the trigonometric functions by which computations having to do with the lengths of lines and the areas of figures can be made. The "function" of an angle, as for instance the sine of an angle, is simply a ratio between certain sides of a right-angled triangle for the particular angle of the triangle considered. Each angle has its own functions. The functions most commonly used are the sine, cosine, tangent, and cotangent. Values of these functions for any angle may be found in tables in an engineering or other handbook or they may be obtained quickly and with a fair degree of accuracy by the slide rule.

In any right-angled triangle the functions of either acute angle of the triangle are:

$$\text{Sine A} = \frac{\text{opposite side}}{\text{hypotenuse}} = \frac{a}{c}$$

$$\text{Cosine A} = \frac{\text{adjacent side}}{\text{hypotenuse}} = \frac{b}{c}$$

$$\text{Tangent A} = \frac{\text{opposite side}}{\text{adjacent side}} = \frac{a}{b}$$

$$\text{Cotangent A} = \frac{\text{adjacent side}}{\text{opposite side}} = \frac{b}{a}$$

The following examples will illustrate the meaning of the above functions. A right-angled triangle has the short side equal to 1, the long side 1.73, and the hypotenuse 2. The acute angles are 30 and 60 degrees.

41

Then $\sin 30° = \dfrac{1}{2} = 0.5$ $\qquad$ $\tan 30° = \dfrac{1}{1.73} = 0.577$

$\qquad$ $\sin 60° = \dfrac{1.73}{2} = 0.866$ $\qquad$ $\tan 60° = \dfrac{1.73}{1} = 1.73$

$\qquad$ $\cos 30° = \dfrac{1.73}{2} = 0.866$ $\qquad$ $\cot 30° = \dfrac{1.73}{1} = 1.73$

$\qquad$ $\cos 60° = \dfrac{1}{2} = 0.5$ $\qquad$ $\cot 60° = \dfrac{1}{1.73} = 0.577$

THE USE OF THE S SCALE IN FINDING SINES

In order to become familiar with the scale of sines on the rule pull out the slide and turn it over so that it is in the position shown by Fig. 23.

The rule now becomes a table of sines, the degrees being on the S scale and the value of the sine for any number of degrees being directly over it on the A scale. It will be noticed that the A scale has a middle division marked 10 on some rules and 1 on other rules. The value of the sine of an angle found at the right of this middle division has a decimal point before it. The value of the sine of an angle at the left of the middle division has a decimal point and zero before it. It is a good plan to mark your rule as in Fig. 23.

.0SIN ‖ 0.SIN

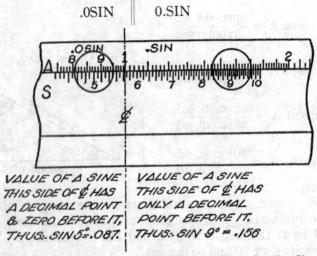

VALUE OF Δ SINE THIS SIDE OF ₵ HAS A DECIMAL POINT & ZERO BEFORE IT, THUS:- SIN 5° = .087.

VALUE OF Δ SINE THIS SIDE OF ₵ HAS ONLY Δ DECIMAL POINT BEFORE IT, THUS:- SIN 9° = .156

Fig. 23. Rule Marked for Locating Decimal Point in Reading Sines

Examples:

Left of Center	Right of Center
sin 2° = 0.0349	sin = 11° = 0.191
sin 8° = 0.139	sin = 25° = 0.423
sin 9.9° = 0.172	sin = 75° = 0.966

The ordinary slide rule does not have markings below 34′ on the S scale. In order to find the sine of an angle below 34′ use the (′) gauge mark which is found on the S scale near the figure 2. To find the sine of 1′ set this gauge mark to 1 on the A scale. Over 90° on S you will find 291 on A. This number should have three zeros before it in order to equal the sine of one minute. Thus: .000291 = sin 1′. As this figure is nearly .0003, for ordinary work it is sufficiently accurate to say,

$$\sin 1' = 0.0003 \text{ (``Three zeros three'')}$$

To find the sine of 5′ set the gauge mark to 5 on A and over the left-hand division on S read 0.00145 = 0.0015 approximately or 5×0.0003.

In order to find the sines of angles measured in seconds, use the gauge mark near 1° marked (″). Place this gauge mark under 1 on the A scale, and find 485 on A over 90° on S. This number should have five zeros before it to equal the sine of 1″ or 0.00000485. As this is approximately 0.000005 we say for ordinary calculations,

$$\sin 1'' = 0.000005 \text{ (``Five zeros five'')}$$

When only a few sines are to be looked up it is not necessary to pull out the slide and turn it over. Turn the whole rule over and note a hairline that goes with the S scale. Pull the slide out until the desired number of degrees on the S scale is opposite the hairline and then roll your rule over. If the S scale and hairline are on the top of your rule you will find the value of the sine on the top when you roll the rule over.

This method of reading sines is clearly shown by Fig. 24.

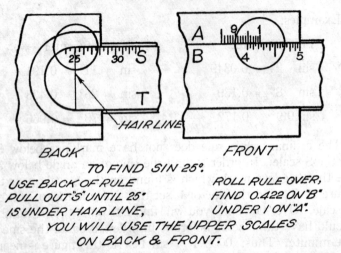

TO FIND SIN 25°.

USE BACK OF RULE
PULL OUT "S" UNTIL 25°
IS UNDER HAIR LINE,

ROLL RULE OVER,
FIND 0.422 ON "B"
UNDER I ON "A".

YOU WILL USE THE UPPER SCALES
ON BACK & FRONT.

Fig. 24. Rule Set for Finding the Sine of an Angle Measured in Degrees

In order to use the gauge mark for minutes without removing the slide and turning it over, set the gauge mark to the hairline on the back of the rule and read sines on A over the number of minutes on B as shown by Fig. 25(a) and (b).

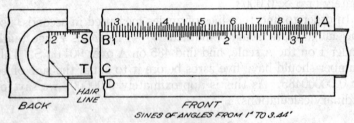

Fig. 25(a). Rule Set for Finding Sines of Angles Measured in Minutes

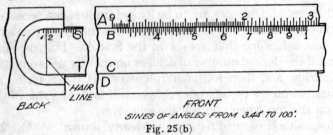

Fig. 25(b)

Use the same procedure in finding the sines of angles measured in seconds, but use the (") gauge mark.

In using gauge marks always remember that sine of 1' has 3 zeros before it; sine of 1" has 5 zeros before it; and place the decimal point accordingly.

COSINES

To find the cosine of an angle look up the sine of the complement of the angle: that is, the sine of 90 degrees minus the given angle.

Examples:

$$\cos 30 = \sin (90° - 30°) = \sin 60° = 0.866$$

$$\cos 44 = \sin (90° - 44°) = \sin 46° = 0.719$$

$$\cos 65 = \sin (90° - 65°) = \sin 25° = 0.423$$

$$\cos 80 = \sin (90° - 80°) = \sin 10° = 0.174$$

USE OF THE T SCALE FOR FINDING TANGENTS

In finding the values of a large number of tangents the slide may be turned over and used in the same manner as the sine or S scale. Usually, however, the slide is not turned over but pulled out to the proper angle which is read under the hairline

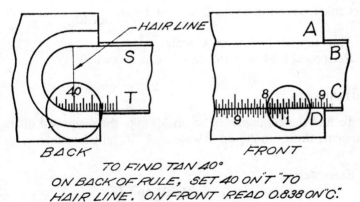

TO FIND TAN 40°
ON BACK OF RULE, SET 40 ON T TO
HAIR LINE. ON FRONT READ 0.838 ON "C."

Fig. 26. Use of T Scale for Finding Tangents

on the back of the rule and the value of the tangent read on the front of the rule.

If the T scale on which the angle is found is on the lower edge of the slide, the value of the tangent will be found on the lower edge of the rule when it is rolled over. This is clearly shown by Fig. 26 .

Examples:

$$\tan 40° = 0.839$$

$$\tan 22° = 0.404$$

$$\tan 15° = 0.268$$

$$\tan \ \ 6° = 0.105$$

To find the value of the tangent of an angle less than 5° 40′, look up the sine of the angle. Thus, the value of the tangent of $20′ = 0.0058$ approximately.

To find the tangent of an angle above 45° read the reciprocal of the tangent of the complement of the angle.

$$\tan 50° = \frac{1}{\tan 40°} = \frac{1}{0.839} = 1.192$$

Set rule to read tan 40° on T scale and read $\frac{1}{\tan 40°}$ on CI scale.

Thus tan 40° = 0.84 on C scale.
Reciprocal 0.84 = 1.192 on CI scale = tan 50°.

COTANGENTS

To find the cotangent of an angle, take the reciprocal of the tangent, thus: tan 30° on T scale = 1.732 on CI scale.

Examples:

$$\cot 40° = 1.192 \text{ on CI}$$

$$\cot 22° = 2.48 \ \text{ on CI}$$

CHAPTER VIII

LOGARITHMS AND THEIR APPLICATION TO THE SLIDE RULE

A logarithm is an exponent or power of a number called the base. The logarithm of a given number is that number which when used as an exponent of the base will raise or lower the base to the given number. In the common or Briggs system of logarithms, the base is always 10. The number 2 is the logarithm of 100 because $10^2 = 100$. Similarly 5 is the logarithm of 100,000 because $10^5 = 100,000$. 0.301 is the logarithm of 2 because $10^{0.301} = 2$.

Mathematicians have prepared tables by which the logarithm of any number may be found. Ordinary tables go to 4 or 6 decimal places and are sufficiently accurate for ordinary work. For extremely accurate work 12-place tables may be obtained.

MULTIPLICATION BY MEANS OF LOGARITHMS

If we take from a table of logarithms the logarithm of 2 = 0.301 and of 3 = 0.477 we could write

$$10^{0.301} \times 10^{0.477} = 10^{0.301 + 0.477} = 10^{0.778}$$

If we look up the number corresponding to 0.778 we find it to be 6. Thus by adding together the logarithms of two numbers and looking up the number corresponding to the sum of the logarithms we find we have multiplied the two numbers. The number corresponding to a logarithm is called the antilogarithm.

In the example just given 0.778 is the logarithm of 6 to the base 10. This is generally read "The logarithm of 6 is 0.778." The fact that it is to the base 10 is ordinarily not mentioned.

If we had the logarithm 0.778 and wanted to know what number had a logarithm of 0.778 we should find from a table of logarithms that the number was 6. The number 6 would be called the antilogarithm of 0.778.

Taking the more difficult problem 2.751 × 8.594

$$\begin{aligned} \text{Log. of } 2.751 &= 0.43949 \\ 8.594 &= 0.93420 \\ \hline \text{Sum} &= 1.37369 \\ \text{Antilog.} &= 23.642 \end{aligned}$$

which is the same answer we should have obtained by multiplying 2.751 by 8.594 by arithmetic. The above problem shows that it is much quicker to look up the logarithms, add them, and look up the antilogarithm than to multiply long numbers. From the above it also appears that four long numbers could have been multiplied together with very little work, whereas the work in multiplying four long numbers by arithmetic is considerable with many chances for error.

In the above examples when multiplying two numbers together we added their logarithms and looked up the number corresponding to their sum, or the antilogarithm. We could just as well have laid out one logarithm on a scale such as D (Fig. 27) and the other on a similar scale C, moved C along D as shown by Fig. 27, and let the scales do the adding. In Fig. 22 the scales are set to multiply 2 × 3. The logarithm of 2 is 0.301 and the logarithm of 3 is 0.477. The 1 of scale C is set over the logarithm of 2 or 0.301 on scale D and on scale C we find that 0.477 the logarithm of 3 is now over 0.778 which is the logarithm of 6. We can now go a step farther and letter the scales C and D with the numbers 2 and 3 instead of the values of the logarithms of these two numbers and letter 0.778 with the number 6.

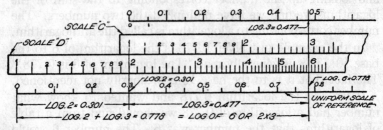

Fig. 27. Logarithms of 2 and 3 Laid Out on Similar Scales and
Added by Sliding Scale C along D

DIVISION BY MEANS OF LOGARITHMS

Using the numbers 3 and 2 again:

$$\frac{3}{2} = \frac{10^{0.477}}{10^{0.301}} = 10^{0.477 - 0.301} = 10^{0.176}$$

The antilogarithm of 0.176 is 1.5 which is the same as $\frac{3}{2}$.

Hence to divide, subtract the logarithm of the divisor from the logarithm of the dividend and look up the antilogarithm of the difference. This number will be the quotient.

The slide rule subtracts the logarithms and gives the quotient. The operation on the rule is the inverse of that used for multiplication as shown by Fig. 27.

The following example will illustrate:

Divide 7 by 2. See Fig. 28.

The logarithm of 7 is 0.845 and the logarithm of 2 is 0.301. The difference as shown on the scales of Fig. 28 is 0.544. The quotient is 3.5 as shown on Scale D, since, as explained under "Multiplication," the scales are lettered as antilogarithms and not logarithms.

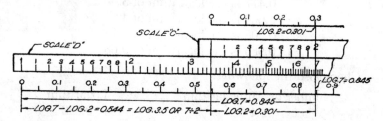

Fig. 28. Setting of Scales C and D to Subtract the Logarithm of 2 from the Logarithm of 7

THE L SCALE

The L or logarithm scale which is engraved on the back of the slide gives the logarithms of the numbers on the C scale found on the front of the slide. To use the L scale, pull it out until a number on the back of the slide is under the hairline on the back of the rule. This number is the logarithm of the number on the C scale that stands over the right-hand 1 on the D scale. For example, in Fig. 29, 301 is under the hairline on the back of the rule; when the rule is rolled over, 2 on C is found over the right-hand 1 on D, so 301 is the logarithm of 2.

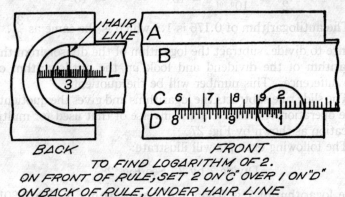

Fig. 29. Finding the Logarithm of a Number on the Slide Rule

Check the following:

> 0.477 is the logarithm of 3
> 0.602 is the logarithm of 4
> 0.908 is the logarithm of 8.1
> 0.986 is the logarithm of 9.68

Check also the following:

Number or Antilogarithm	Logarithm
2.1	0.322
5.6	0.748
8.7	0.940
9.2	0.964

USING LOGARITHMS

Logarithms can be used for multiplying and dividing numbers as explained on pages 47 and 49. But this is not necessary on the slide rule because the C and D scales are divided in proportion to the logarithms of the numbers they represent.

Thus, when C is used with D as explained under multiplication and division, the rule mechanically performs the operations of multiplying and dividing.

Logarithms must be used with the ordinary slide rule to find fractional powers and roots of numbers, as for instance $2^{0.3}$ or $\sqrt[2.5]{75}$. In order to find fractional powers and roots of numbers a knowledge of the following brief theory of logarithms is necessary.

A logarithm consists of two parts, the mantissa and the characteristic. The mantissa is the part found on the L scale of the rule. The characteristic is a number used with the mantissa whose value is determined from the number of digits to the left of the decimal point in a whole or mixed number, and from the number of zeros between the decimal point and the first significant figure in a decimal fraction.

In a whole or mixed number the characteristic is one less than the number of digits to the left of the decimal point, as for instance:

Number	Characteristic	Mantissa from L Scale	Complete Logarithm
352.	2	547	2.547
25.2	1	401	1.401
2.08	0	318	0.318

In a decimal fraction the characteristic is one more than the number of zeros between the decimal point and the first significant figure and it has a minus sign. Either the minus sign is written directly over the characteristic, meaning that it applies only to the characteristic, or the characteristic is written as a number with -10 after it. The number is taken of such a value that when -10 is used with it, it will give the desired minus value of characteristic.

The following will illustrate:

Number	Characteristic	Mantissa from L Scale	Complete Logarithm
0.0075	$\bar{3}$	875	$\bar{3}.875$ or $7.875 -10$
0.09	$\bar{2}$	954	$\bar{2}.954$ or $8.954 -10$
0.92	$\bar{1}$	964	$\bar{1}.964$ or $9.964 -10$

RAISING A NUMBER TO A POWER BY LOGARITHMS

Find the mantissa of the number on the L scale. Supply the proper characteristic. Multiply the complete logarithm by the power: the product will be a logarithm whose mantissa will be on the L scale.

Find this mantissa on the L scale and the antilogarithm or number corresponding to the logarithm on the C scale. The number on the C scale will be the given number raised to the desired power. The following will illustrate:

Number and Power	Man-tissa	Char-acter-istic	Logarithm Times Power	Required No. (Anti-logarithm)
4^2	602	0	$0.602 \times 2 = 1.204$	16.
$12^{3.6}$	0792	1	$1.0792 \times 3.6 = 3.885$	7674.
$0.06^{2.1}$	778	$\overline{2}$	$(8.778 - 10)\,2.1 =$ $18.434 - 21 = 7.434 - 10$	0.00272
$4^{0.5}$	602	0	$0.602 \times 0.5 = 0.301$	2.
$45^{0.3}$	653	1	$1.653 \times 0.3 = 0.496$	3.133
$0.52^{2.45}$	716	$\overline{1}$	$(9.716 - 10)\,2.45 =$ $(99.716 - 100)\,2.45 =$ $244.3042 - 245 = 9.3042 - 10$	0.2015

FINDING THE ROOT OF A NUMBER BY LOGARITHMS

Find the mantissa on the L scale. Supply the proper characteristic. Divide the complete logarithm by the root. Find the antilogarithm.

Number and Root	Man-tissa	Char-acter-istic	Logarithm Divided by Root	Required No. (Anti-logarithm)
$\sqrt[3]{64}$	806	1	$1.806 \div 3 = 0.602$	4.
$\sqrt[3.5]{950}$	978	2	$2.978 \div 3.5 = 0.851$	7.092
$\sqrt[0.2]{3.8}$	580	0	$0.580 \div 0.2 = 2.90$	792.

PART TWO

WELL-KNOWN SLIDE RULES EXPLAINED BY CHARTS AND SAMPLE SETTINGS

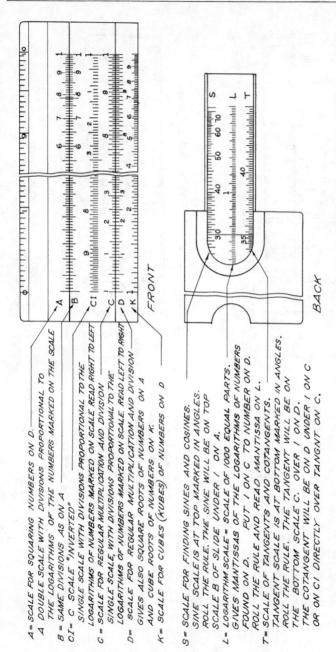

A = SCALE FOR SQUARING NUMBERS ON D.
    A DOUBLE SCALE WITH DIVISIONS PROPORTIONAL TO
    THE LOGARITHMS OF THE NUMBERS MARKED ON THE SCALE

B = SAME DIVISIONS AS ON A

CI = C SCALE "INVERTED"
    SINGLE SCALE WITH DIVISIONS PROPORTIONAL TO THE
    LOGARITHMS OF NUMBERS MARKED ON SCALE READ RIGHT TO LEFT

C = SCALE FOR REGULAR MULTIPLICATION AND DIVISION
    SINGLE SCALE WITH DIVISIONS PROPORTIONAL TO THE
    LOGARITHMS OF NUMBERS MARKED ON SCALE. READ LEFT TO RIGHT

D = SCALE FOR REGULAR MULTIPLICATION AND DIVISION
    GIVES ALSO SQUARE ROOTS OF NUMBERS ON A
    AND CUBE ROOTS OF NUMBERS ON K.

K = SCALE FOR CUBES (KUBES) OF NUMBERS ON D

FRONT

S = SCALE FOR FINDING SINES AND COSINES.
    SINE SCALE IS AT TOP MARKED IN ANGLES.
    ROLL THE RULE, THE SINE WILL BE ON TOP
    SCALE B OF SLIDE UNDER 1 ON A.

L = LOGARITHM SCALE = SCALE OF 1000 EQUAL PARTS.
    GIVES MANTISSAS OF THE LOGARITHMS OF NUMBERS
    FOUND ON D.   PUT 1 ON C TO NUMBER ON D.
    ROLL THE RULE AND READ MANTISSA ON L.

T = SCALE OF TANGENTS AND COTANGENTS.
    TANGENT SCALE IS AT BOTTOM MARKED IN ANGLES.
    ROLL THE RULE. THE TANGENT WILL BE ON
    THE BOTTOM SCALE C. OVER 1 ON D.
    THE COTANGENT WILL BE ON D UNDER 1 ON C
    OR ON CI DIRECTLY OVER TANGNT ON C.

BACK

THE POLYPHASE SLIDE RULE
SEE COMPLETE DISCUSSION AND PROBLEMS IN TEXT

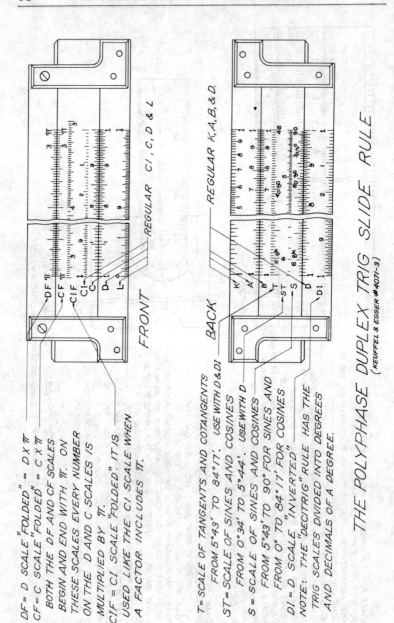

FRONT

REGULAR CI, C, D & L

BACK

REGULAR K, A, B, & D.

DF = D SCALE "FOLDED" = D X π
CF = C SCALE "FOLDED" = C X π
    BOTH THE DF AND CF SCALES
    BEGIN AND END WITH π. ON
    THESE SCALES EVERY NUMBER
    ON THE D AND C SCALES IS
    MULTIPLIED BY π.
CIF = CI SCALE "FOLDED". IT IS
    USED LIKE THE CI SCALE WHEN
    A FACTOR INCLUDES π.

T = SCALE OF TANGENTS AND COTANGENTS
    FROM 5°43' TO 84°17'. USE WITH D & DI
ST = SCALE OF SINES AND COSINES
    FROM 0°34' TO 5°44'. USE WITH D
S = SCALE OF SINES AND COSINES
    FROM 5°43' TO 90° FOR SINES AND
    FROM 0° TO 84°17' FOR COSINES
DI = D SCALE "INVERTED"
NOTE: THE "DECITRIG" RULE HAS THE
    TRIG SCALES DIVIDED INTO DEGREES
    AND DECIMALS OF A DEGREE.

THE POLYPHASE DUPLEX TRIG SLIDE RULE
(KEUFFEL & ESSER #4071-3)

POLYPHASE DUPLEX TRIG SLIDE RULE

Note: The Polyphase Duplex Decitrig Slide Rule is the same except that the divisions are decimal.

SAMPLE SETTINGS

MULTIPLICATION, DIVISION, POWERS, ROOTS, AND LOGARITHMS

Scales A, B, C, D, C1, K, and L same as regular polyphase slide rule. See pp. 3-52 and plate p. 55.

MULTIPLICATION AND DIVISION OF NUMBERS CONTAINING THE FACTOR π

The DF scale known as the "folded" scale contains the factor π.

Multiply 2.62 by π.

On front of rule set hairline of runner to 2.62 on D.

On front of rule on DF, under hairline read 8.23.

Divide 82 by π.

On front of rule set hairline of runner to 82 on DF.

On front of rule on D, under hairline read 26.1.

Find the area of a circle whose diameter is $2\frac{1}{4}$". Use formula $A = \pi r^2$, $r = 1.125$".

On front of rule multiply 1.125 by 1.125 and get $1.266 = r^2$.

On front of rule set hairline of runner to 1.266 on D.

On front of rule on DF read 3.98 square inches.

POLYPHASE DUPLEX TRIG SLIDE RULE
CONTINUED ON PAGE 59

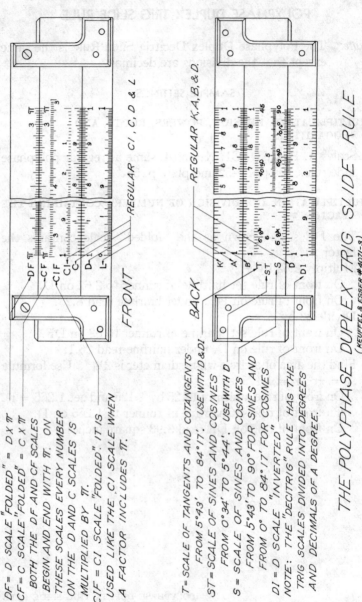

FRONT

REGULAR CI, C, D & L

BACK

REGULAR K, A, B, & D.

DF = D SCALE "FOLDED" = D X π
CF = C SCALE "FOLDED" = C X π
BOTH THE DF AND CF SCALES
BEGIN AND END WITH π. ON
THESE SCALES EVERY NUMBER
ON THE D AND C SCALES IS
MULTIPLIED BY π.
CIF = CI SCALE "FOLDED". IT IS
USED LIKE THE CI SCALE WHEN
A FACTOR INCLUDES π.

T = SCALE OF TANGENTS AND COTANGENTS
    FROM 5°43' TO 84°17'.   USE WITH D & D1
ST = SCALE OF SINES AND COSINES
    FROM 0°34' TO 5°44'.   USE WITH D
S = SCALE OF SINES AND COSINES
    FROM 5°43' TO 90° FOR SINES AND
    FROM 0° TO 84°17' FOR COSINES
D1 = D SCALE "INVERTED"
NOTE: THE "DECITRIG" RULE HAS THE
    TRIG SCALES DIVIDED INTO DEGREES
    AND DECIMALS OF A DEGREE.

THE POLYPHASE DUPLEX TRIG SLIDE RULE
(KEUFFEL & ESSER #4071-3)

POLYPHASE DUPLEX TRIG SLIDE RULE—Continued

TANGENTS AND COTANGENTS

Find tangent of 10° 40'.

On back of rule set hairline of runner to 10° 40' (black figures) on T.

On back of rule on D, under hairline read 0.1883.

Find tangent of 80° 20'.

On back of rule set hairline of runner to 80° 20' (red figures) on T.

On back of rule on DI (red figures) under hairline read 5.87.

Find cotangent of 10° 40'.

On back of rule set hairline of runner to 10° 40' (black figures) on T.

On back of rule on DI (red figures) under hairline read 5.31.

Find cotangent of 80° 20'.

On back of rule set hairline of runner to 80° 20' (red figures) on T.

On back of rule on D, under hairline read 0.1703.

SMALL ANGLES TANGENTS AND COTANGENTS

Find tangent of 2° 30'.

On back of rule set hairline of runner to 2° 30' on ST.

On back of rule on D, under hairline read 0.0437.

Cotangent will be on DI (red figures) = 22.9.

SINES AND COSINES

Find sine of 36° 30'.

On back of rule set hairline of runner to 36° 30' (black figures) on S.

On back of rule on D, under hairline read 0.595.

Find cosine of 66° 30'.

On back of rule set hairline of runner to 66° 30' (red figures) on S.

On back of rule on D, under hairline read 0.399.

POLYPHASE DUPLEX TRIG SLIDE RULE
CONTINUED ON PAGE 61

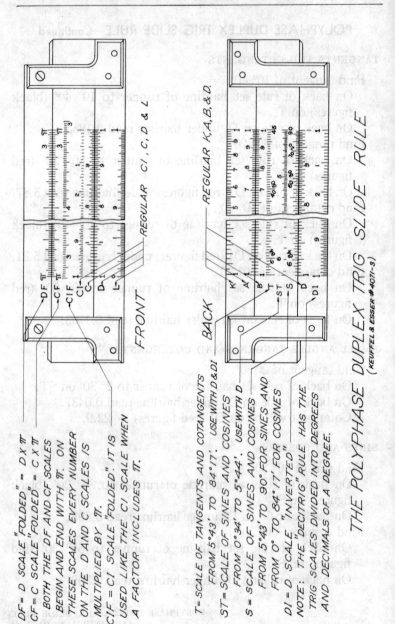

DF = D SCALE "FOLDED" = D X π
CF = C SCALE "FOLDED" = C X π
BOTH THE DF AND CF SCALES
BEGIN AND END WITH π. ON
THESE SCALES EVERY NUMBER
ON THE D AND C SCALES IS
MULTIPLIED BY π.
CIF = CI SCALE "FOLDED". IT IS
USED LIKE THE CI SCALE WHEN
A FACTOR INCLUDES π.

REGULAR CI, C, D & L

FRONT

REGULAR K,A,B,& D.

BACK

T = SCALE OF TANGENTS AND COTANGENTS
    FROM 5°43' TO 84°17'. USE WITH D&DI
ST = SCALE OF SINES AND COSINES
    FROM 0°34' TO 5°44'. USE WITH D
S = SCALE OF SINES AND COSINES
    FROM 5°43' TO 90° FOR SINES AND
    FROM 0° TO 84°17' FOR COSINES
DI = D SCALE "INVERTED". IT IS
NOTE: THE "DECITRIG" RULE HAS THE
    TRIG SCALES DIVIDED INTO DEGREES
    AND DECIMALS OF A DEGREE.

THE POLYPHASE DUPLEX TRIG SLIDE RULE
(KEUFFEL & ESSER # 4071-3)

POLYPHASE DUPLEX TRIG SLIDE RULE—Continued

SMALL ANGLES SINES AND COSINES

Find sine of 2° 30′.

On back of rule set hairline of runner to 2° 30′ on ST.

On back of rule on D, under hairline read 0.0436.

Cosines of small angles on this scale are practically 1 (0.99995 for 35′ and 0.99511 for 5° 40′).

RIGHT TRIANGLES AND COMPLEX QUANTITIES AS Z = R ±jX

Find hypotenuse when base = 4, altitude = 3.

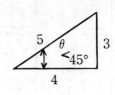

Set right index of S to 4 on D.

Over 3 on D read 36.9° (black) on T (means 4 × tan 36.9° = 3 or 4 × $\frac{3}{4}$ = 3).

Next bring 36.9° (black) on S to 3 on D and under right index of S read 5 on D (means 3 ÷ sin 36.9° = 5 or 3 ÷ $\frac{3}{5}$ = 5).

Use   Black S
      Black T

Find hypotenuse when base = 3, altitude = 4.

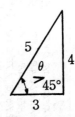

Set right index of S to 4 on D.

Over 3 on D read 53.13° (red) on T (means 4 × cot 53.13° = 3 or 4 × $\frac{3}{4}$ = 3).

Next bring 53.13° (red) on S to 3 on D and under right index of S read 5 on D (means 3 ÷ cot 53.13° = 5 or 3 ÷ $\frac{3}{5}$ = 5).

Use   Red S = cos
      Red T = cot

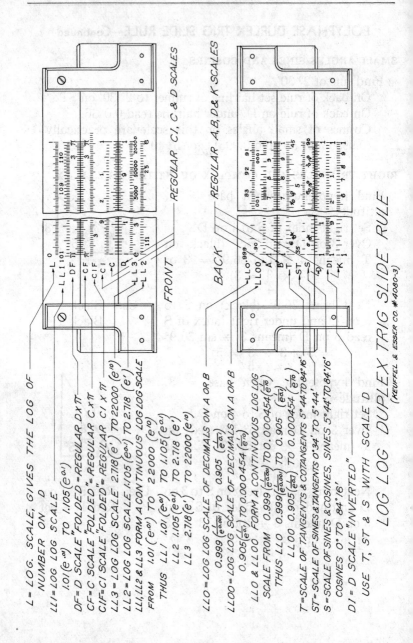

LOG LOG DUPLEX TRIG SLIDE RULE

SAMPLE SETTINGS

MULTIPLICATION, DIVISION, POWERS, ROOTS, AND LOGARITHMS

Scales A, B, C, D, CI, K, and L same as regular polyphase slide rule. See pp. 3-52 and plate p. 55.

MULTIPLICATION AND DIVISION OF NUMBERS CONTAINING THE FACTOR π

The DF scale known as the "folded" scale contains the factor π.

Multiply 2.62 by π.

On front of rule set hairline of runner to 2.62 on D.

On front of rule on DF, under hairline read 8.23.

Divide 82 by π.

On front of rule set hairline of runner to 82 on DF.

On front of rule on D, under hairline read 26.1.

Find the area of a circle whose diameter is $2\frac{1}{4}''$. Use formula $A = \pi r^2$, $r = 1.125''$.

On front of rule multiply 1.125 by 1.125 and get $1.266 = r^2$.

On front of rule set hairline of runner to 1.266 on D.

On front of rule on DF read 3.98 square inches.

LOG LOG DUPLEX TRIG SLIDE RULE
CONTINUED ON PAGE 65

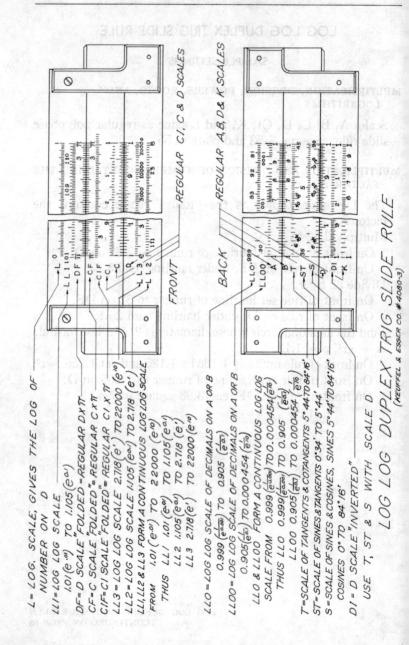

L = LOG. SCALE, GIVES THE LOG OF NUMBER ON D

LLI = LOG LOG SCALE

1.01 (e^.01) TO 1.105 (e^.1)

DF = D SCALE "FOLDED" = REGULAR D x π

CF = C SCALE "FOLDED" = REGULAR C x π

CIF = CI SCALE "FOLDED" = REGULAR CI x π

LL3 = LOG LOG SCALE 2.718 (e^1) TO 22000 (e^10)

LL2 = LOG LOG SCALE 1.105 (e^.1) TO 2.718 (e^1)

LL1, LL2 & LL3 FORM A CONTINUOUS LOG LOG SCALE

FROM   1.01 (e^.01) TO   22000 (e^10)

THUS   LL1   1.01 (e^.01)   TO 1.105 (e^.1)

       LL2   1.105 (e^.1)   TO 2.718 (e^1)

       LL3   2.718 (e^1)   TO 22000 (e^10)

LLO = LOG LOG SCALE OF DECIMALS ON A OR B

0.999 (1/e^.001) TO 0.905 (1/e^.1)

LLOO = LOG LOG SCALE OF DECIMALS ON A OR B

0.905 (1/e^.1) TO 0.000454 (1/e^10)

LLO & LLOO FORM A CONTINUOUS LOG LOG

SCALE FROM   0.999 (1/e^.001) TO 0.000454 (1/e^10)

THUS   LLO   0.999 (1/e^.001) TO 0.905 (1/e^.1)

      LLOO   0.905 (1/e^.1)   TO 0.000454 (1/e^10)

T = SCALE OF TANGENTS & COTANGENTS 5° 44' TO 84° 16'

ST = SCALE OF SINES & TANGENTS 0° 34' TO 5° 44'

S = SCALE OF SINES & COSINES, SINES 5° 44' TO 84° 16'

COSINES 0° TO 84° 16'

DI = D SCALE "INVERTED"

USE T, ST & S WITH SCALE D

LOG LOG DUPLEX TRIG SLIDE RULE

(KEUFFEL & ESSER CO. #4080-3)

LOG LOG DUPLEX TRIG SLIDE RULE—Continued

TANGENTS AND COTANGENTS

Find tangent of 10° 40′.

On back of rule set hairline of runner to 10° 40′ (black figures) on T.

On back of rule on D, under hairline read 0.1883.

Find tangent of 80° 20′.

On back of rule set hairline of runner to 80° 20′ (red figures) on T.

On back of rule on DI (red figures) under hairline read 5.87.

Find cotangent of 10° 40′.

On back of rule set hairline of runner to 10° 40′ (black figures) on T.

On back of rule on DI (red figures) under hairline read 5.31.

Find cotangent of 80° 20′.

On back of rule set hairline of runner to 80° 20′ (red figures) on T.

On back of rule on D, under hairline read 0.1703.

SMALL ANGLES TANGENTS AND COTANGENTS

Find tangent of 2° 30′.

On back of rule set hairline of runner to 2° 30′ on ST.

On back of rule on D, under hairline read 0.0437.

Cotangent will be on DI (red figures) = 22.9.

SINES AND COSINES

Find sine of 36° 30′.

On back of rule set hairline of runner to 36° 30′ (black figures) on S.

On back of rule on D, under hairline read 0.595.

Find cosine of 66° 30′.

On back of rule set hairline of runner to 66° 30′ (red figures) on S.

On back of rule on D, under hairline read 0.399.

LOG LOG DUPLEX TRIG SLIDE RULE
CONTINUED ON PAGE 67

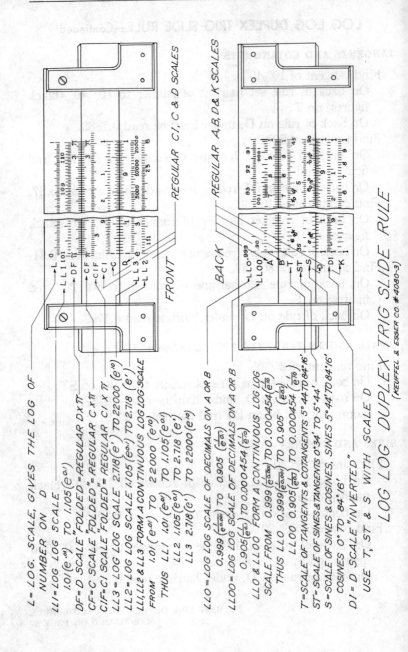

L = LOG. SCALE, GIVES THE LOG OF NUMBER ON D

LL1 = LOG LOG SCALE
1.01(e^.01) TO 1.105(e^.1)

DF = D SCALE "FOLDED" = REGULAR D x π

CF = C SCALE "FOLDED" = REGULAR C x π

CIF = CI SCALE "FOLDED" = REGULAR CI x π

LL3 = LOG LOG SCALE 2.718(e') TO 22000 (e^10)

LL2 = LOG LOG SCALE 1.105(e^.1) TO 2.718 (e')

LL1, LL2 & LL3 FORM A CONTINUOUS LOG LOG SCALE

FROM 1.01 (e^.01) TO 22000 (e^10)

THUS LL1 1.01 (e^.01) TO 1.105(e^.1)
LL2 1.105 (e^.1) TO 2.718 (e')
LL3 2.718 (e') TO 22000 (e^10)

LL0 = LOG LOG SCALE OF DECIMALS ON A OR B
0.999 (e^.001) to 0.905 (1/(e^.1))

LL00 = LOG LOG SCALE OF DECIMALS ON A OR B
0.905 (1/(e^.1)) TO 0.000454 (1/(e^10))

LL0 & LL00 FORM A CONTINUOUS LOG LOG SCALE FROM 0.999 (e^.001) TO 0.000454 (1/(e^10))

THUS LL0 0.999 (1/(e^.001)) TO 0.905 (1/(e^.1))
LL00 0.905 (1/(e^.1)) TO 0.000454 (1/(e^10))

T = SCALE OF TANGENTS & COTANGENTS 5° 44' TO 84° 6'

ST = SCALE OF SINES & TANGENTS 0° 34' TO 5° 44'

S = SCALE OF SINES & COSINES, SINES 5° 44' TO 84° 6'
COSINES 0° TO 84° 16'

DI = D SCALE "INVERTED"

USE T, ST & S WITH SCALE D

FRONT — REGULAR CI, C & D SCALES

BACK — REGULAR A, B, D & K SCALES

LOG LOG DUPLEX TRIG SLIDE RULE
(KEUFFEL & ESSER CO. #4080-3)

LOG LOG DUPLEX TRIG SLIDE RULE—Continued

SMALL ANGLES SINES AND COSINES

Find sine of 2° 30′.

On back of rule set hairline of runner to 2° 30′ on ST.

On back of rule on D, under hairline read 0.0436.

Cosines of small angles on this scale are practically 1 (0.99995 for 35′ and 0.99511 for 5° 40′).

RIGHT TRIANGLES AND COMPLEX QUANTITIES AS Z = R ± jX

Find hypotenuse when base = 4, altitude = 3.

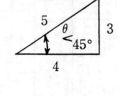

Set right index of S to 4 on D.

Over 3 on D read 36.9° (black) on T (means 4 × tan 36.9° = 3 or 4 × $\frac{3}{4}$ = 3).

Next bring 36.9° (black) on S to 3 on D and under right index of S read 5 on D (means 3 ÷ sin 36.9° = 5 or 3 ÷ $\frac{3}{5}$ = 5).

Use Black S
Black T

Find hypotenuse when base = 3, altitude = 4.

Set right index of S to 4 on D.

Over 3 on D read 53.13° (red) on T (means 4 × cot 53.13° = 3 or 4 × $\frac{3}{4}$ = 3).

Next bring 53.13° (red) on S to 3 on D and under right index of S read 5 on D (means 3 ÷ cot 53.13° = 5 or 3 ÷ $\frac{3}{5}$ = 5).

Use Red S = cos
Red T = cot

LOG LOG DUPLEX TRIG SLIDE RULE
CONTINUED ON PAGE 69

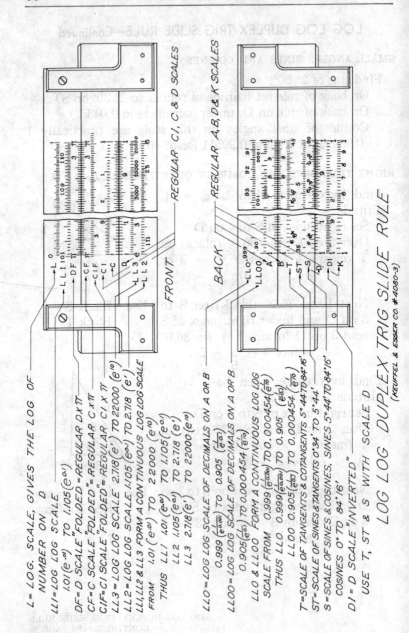

L = LOG. SCALE, GIVES THE LOG OF NUMBER ON D

LLI = LOG LOG SCALE

1.01 ($e^{.01}$) TO 1.105 ($e^{.1}$)

DF = D SCALE "FOLDED" = REGULAR D x π

CF = C SCALE "FOLDED" = REGULAR C x π

CIF = CI SCALE "FOLDED" = REGULAR CI x π

LL3 = LOG LOG SCALE 2.718 (e') TO 22000 (e^{10})

LL2 = LOG LOG SCALE 1.105 ($e^{0.1}$) TO 2.718 (e')

LLI,LL2 & LL3 FORM A CONTINUOUS LOGLOG SCALE

FROM 1.01 ($e^{.01}$) TO 22000 (e^{10})

THUS LL1 1.01 ($e^{.01}$) TO 1.105 ($e^{0.1}$)

LL2 1.105 ($e^{0.1}$) TO 2.718 (e')

LL3 2.718 (e') TO 22000 (e^{10})

REGULAR CI, C & D SCALES

FRONT

REGULAR A,B, D & K SCALES

BACK

LLO = LOG LOG SCALE OF DECIMALS ON A OR B

0.999 ($e^{\frac{1}{0.00}}$) TO 0.905 ($e^{\frac{1}{0.1}}$)

LLOO = LOG LOG SCALE OF DECIMALS ON A OR B

0.905 ($e^{\frac{1}{0.1}}$) TO 0.000454 ($e^{\frac{1}{10}}$)

LLO & LLOO FORM A CONTINUOUS LOG LOG

SCALE FROM 0.999 ($e^{\frac{1}{0.00}}$) TO 0.000454 ($e^{\frac{1}{10}}$)

THUS LLO 0.999 ($e^{\frac{1}{0.00}}$) TO 0.905 ($e^{\frac{1}{0.1}}$)

LLOO 0.905 ($e^{\frac{1}{0.1}}$) TO 0.000454 ($e^{\frac{1}{10}}$)

T = SCALE OF TANGENTS & COTANGENTS 5° 44′ TO 84° 16′

ST = SCALE OF SINES & TANGENTS 0° 34′ TO 5° 44′

S = SCALE OF SINES & COSINES, SINES 5° 44′ TO 84° 16′

COSINES 0° TO 84° 16′

DI = D SCALE "INVERTED"

USE T, ST & S WITH SCALE D

LOG LOG DUPLEX TRIG SLIDE RULE

(KEUFFEL & ESSER CO. #4080-3)

LOG LOG DUPLEX TRIG SLIDE RULE—Continued

LOG LOG SCALES

LL1 1.01($\epsilon^{0.01}$) TO 1.105($\epsilon^{0.1}$)

Find log of 1.02 to base ϵ.
  Set indexes to zero.
  Set runner to 1.02 on LL1.
  Under hairline of runner on C read $\log_\epsilon$ 1.02 = 0.0198.
  On LL1 the decimal point will be .0L, thus 0.0198 (see sketch p. 71).
Find 1.02^2.
  Set 1 on C to 1.02 on LL1.
  Bring runner to power 2 on C.
  Under hairline of runner read 1.0404 on LL1.

Find $\sqrt[3]{1.065}$.
  Set runner to 1.065 on LL1.
  Bring root 3 on C to hairline of runner.
  Opposite 1 on C read 1.0212 on LL1.

LL2 1.105($\epsilon^{0.1}$) TO 2.718(ϵ)

Find log of 1.25 to base ϵ.
  Set indexes to zero.
  Set runner to 1.25 on LL2.
  Under hairline of runner on C, read $\log_\epsilon$ 1.25 = 0.223.
  On LL2 the decimal point will be 0.L, thus 0.223 (see sketch p. 71).
Find $1.16^{3.4}$.
  Set 1 on C to 1.16 on LL2.
  Bring runner to power 3.4 on C.
  Under hairline of runner read 1.656 on LL2.
Find $\sqrt[2.4]{2.1}$.
  Set runner to 2.1 on LL2.
  Bring root 2.4 on C to hairline of runner.
  Opposite 1 on C read 1.362 on LL2.

LOG LOG DUPLEX TRIG SLIDE RULE
CONTINUED ON PAGE 71

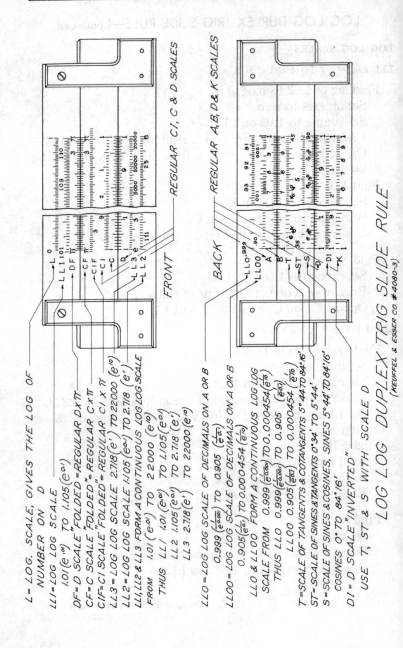

L = LOG. SCALE, GIVES THE LOG OF
NUMBER ON D

LLI = LOG LOG SCALE
1.01($e^{.01}$) TO 1.105($e^{.01}$)

DF = D SCALE "FOLDED" = REGULAR D x π

CF = C SCALE "FOLDED" = REGULAR C x π

CIF = CI SCALE FOLDED = REGULAR CI x π

LL3 = LOG LOG SCALE 2.718(e^1) TO 22000 (e^{10})

LL2 = LOG LOG SCALE 1.105($e^{0.1}$) TO 2.718 (e^1)

LL1, LL2 & LL3 FORM A CONTINUOUS LOG LOG SCALE

FROM   1.01 ($e^{.01}$) TO   22000 (e^{10})

THUS   LL1   1.01 ($e^{.01}$)   TO 1.105($e^{.01}$)
     LL2   1.105   2.718 (e^1)
     LL3   2.718 (e^1)   TO 22000 (e^{10})

LLO = LOG LOG SCALE OF DECIMALS ON A OR B
0.999 ($e^{.001}$) TO 0.905 ($\frac{1}{e^{.1}}$)

LLOO = LOG LOG SCALE OF DECIMALS ON A OR B
0.905($\frac{1}{e^{.1}}$) TO 0.000454 ($\frac{1}{e^{10}}$)

LLO & LLOO FORM A CONTINUOUS LOG LOG
SCALE FROM   0.999 ($e^{.001}$) TO 0.000454 (e^{10})

THUS LLO   0.999 ($e^{.001}$) TO 0.905 ($\frac{1}{e^{.1}}$)

    LLOO   0.905 ($\frac{1}{e^{.1}}$) TO 0.000454 ($\frac{1}{e^{10}}$)

T = SCALE OF TANGENTS & COTANGENTS 5° 44' TO 84° 6'

ST = SCALE OF SINES & TANGENTS 0° 34' TO 5° 44'

S = SCALE OF SINES & COSINES, SINES 5° 44' TO 84° 6'
COSINES 0° TO 84° 16'

DI = D SCALE "INVERTED"
USE T, ST & S WITH SCALE D

REGULAR CI, C & D SCALES

FRONT

REGULAR A, B, D & K SCALES

BACK

LOG LOG DUPLEX TRIG SLIDE RULE
(KEUFFEL & ESSER CO. #4080-3)

LOG LOG DUPLEX TRIG SLIDE RULE—Continued

LL3 2.718(ϵ) TO 22000$+$(ϵ^{10})

Find log of 10 to base ϵ.

    Set indexes to zero.

    Set runner to 10 on LL3.

    Under hairline of runner on C, read $\log_\epsilon$ 10 = 2.3.

    On LL3 the decimal point will be L., thus, 2.3 (see sketch).

Find 15.3^2.

    Set 1 on C to 15.3 on LL3.

    Bring runner to power 2 on C.

    Under hairline of runner read 234 on LL3.

Find $\sqrt[3.2]{68}$.

    Set runner to 68 on LL3.

    Bring root 3.2 on C to hairline of runner.

    Opposite 1 on C, read 3.74 on LL3.

The LL0 scale is used with the A (or B) scale. Numbers on the LL0 scale have their cologarithms to the base ϵ on the A or B scale.

Find log of 0.995 to the base ϵ.

    Set runner to .995 on LL0.

    Under hairline of runner read 0.005 on A.

    0.005 is the colog. of 0.995 to the base ϵ.

    So $\log_\epsilon$ 0.995 = (10 − 10) − 0.005 = 9.995 − 10.

    On LL0 .999 to .99 the decimal point is .00 colog, thus 0.005 (see sketch).

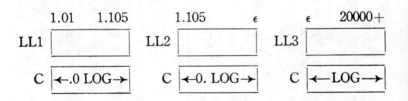

LOG LOG DUPLEX TRIG SLIDE RULE
CONTINUED ON PAGE 73

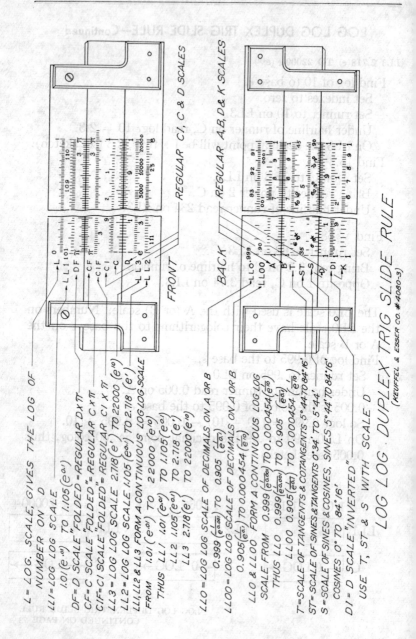

L = LOG. SCALE, GIVES THE LOG OF
NUMBER ON D

LLI = LOG LOG SCALE.
1.01 (e^.01) TO 1.105 (e^.01)

DF = D SCALE "FOLDED" = REGULAR D×π

CF = C SCALE "FOLDED" = REGULAR C×π

CIF = CI SCALE "FOLDED" = REGULAR CI × π

LL3 = LOG LOG SCALE 2.718 (e') TO 22000 (e^10)

LL2 = LOG LOG SCALE 1.105 (e^.01) TO 2.718 (e')

LLI, LL2 & LL3 FORM A CONTINUOUS LOG LOG SCALE
FROM 1.01 (e^.01) TO 2.2000 (e^10)

THUS LLI 1.01 (e^.01) TO 1.105 (e^.01)
LL2 1.105 (e^.01) TO 2.718 (e')
LL3 2.718 (e') TO 22000 (e^10)

REGULAR CI, C & D SCALES

FRONT

REGULAR A, B, D & K SCALES

BACK

LLO = LOG LOG SCALE OF DECIMALS ON A OR B
0.999 (e^.001) TO 0.905 (e^.01)

LLOO = LOG LOG SCALE OF DECIMALS ON A OR B
0.905 (1/e^.01) TO 0.000454 (e^10)

LLO & LLOO FORM A CONTINUOUS LOG LOG
SCALE FROM 0.999 (e^.001) TO 0.000454 (e^10)
THUS LLO 0.999 (e^.001) TO 0.905 (e^.01)
LLOO 0.905 (e^.01) TO 0.000454 (e^10)

T = SCALE OF TANGENTS & COTANGENTS 5° 44' TO 84° 16'.

ST = SCALE OF SINES & TANGENTS 0° 34' TO 5° 44'.

S = SCALE OF SINES & COSINES, SINES 5° 44' TO 84° 16'
COSINES 0° TO 84° 16'

DI = D SCALE "INVERTED"
USE T, ST & S WITH SCALE D

LOG LOG DUPLEX TRIG SLIDE RULE

(KEUFFEL & ESSER CO. #4080-3)

LOG LOG DUPLEX TRIG SLIDE RULE—Continued

LL00 .905 $\left(\dfrac{1}{\epsilon^{0.1}}\right)$ **TO .000454** $\left(\dfrac{1}{\epsilon^{10}}\right)$

The LL00 scale is used with the A (or B) scale. Numbers on the LL00 scale have their cologarithms to the base ϵ on the A or B scale.

Find log 0.8 to the base ϵ.

   Set runner to .8 on LL00.

   Under hairline of runner read 0.223 on A.

   0.223 is the colog. of 0.8 to the base ϵ.

   So $\log_\epsilon$ 0.8 = (10 − 10) − 0.223 = 9.777 − 10.

   On LL00 .905 to .37 the decimal point is .colog, thus 0.223 (see sketch).

Find $\log_\epsilon$ 0.05.

   Set runner to 0.05 on LL00.

   Under hairline of runner read 3 on A.

   3 is the colog. of 0.05 to the base ϵ.

   So $\log_\epsilon$ 0.05 = (10 − 10) − 3 = 7.00 − 10.

   On LL00 .37 to .000454 the decimal point is colog., thus 3. (see sketch).

Find $0.075^{1.4}$.

   Set 1 on A to .075 on LL00.

   Bring runner to power 1.4 on A.

   Under hairline of runner read 0.0266 on LL00.

Find $\sqrt[3.7]{0.14}$.

   Set runner to .14 on LL00.

   Bring root 3.7 on B to hairline of runner.

   Opposite 1 on B read 0.588 on LL00.

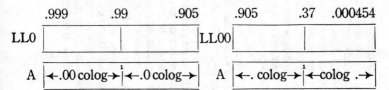

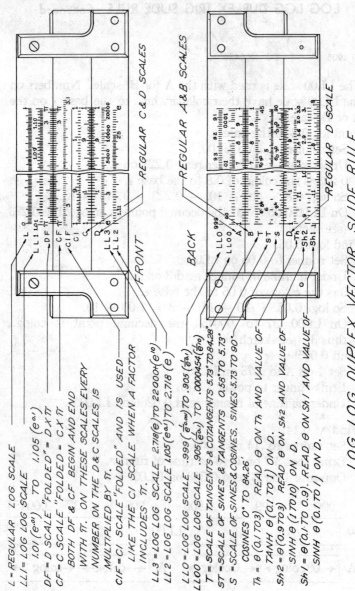

L = REGULAR LOG LOG SCALE

LL1 = LOG LOG SCALE
1.01 ($e^{.01}$) TO 1.105 ($e^{.1}$)

DF = D SCALE "FOLDED" = D × π

CF = C SCALE "FOLDED" = C × π
BOTH DF & CF BEGIN AND END
WITH π. ON THESE SCALES EVERY
NUMBER ON THE D & C SCALES IS
MULTIPLIED BY π.

CIF = CI SCALE "FOLDED" AND IS USED
LIKE THE CI SCALE WHEN A FACTOR
INCLUDES π.

LL3 = LOG LOG SCALE 2.718(e) TO 22000(e^{10})

LL2 = LOG LOG SCALE 1.105 ($e^{.1}$) TO 2.718 (e)

LLO = LOG LOG SCALE .999 ($e^{-.001}$) TO .905 ($e^{-.1}$)

LL00 = LOG LOG SCALE .905($e^{-.1}$) TO .000454(e^{-10})

T = SCALE OF TANGENTS & COTANGENTS 5.73° TO 84.28°

ST = SCALE OF SINES & TANGENTS 0.58° TO 5.73°

S = SCALE OF SINES & COSINES, SINES 5.73 TO 90
COSINES 0° TO 84.26'

Th = θ (0.1 TO 3). READ θ ON Th AND VALUE OF
TANH θ (0.1 TO 1) ON D.

Sh2 = θ (0.9703) READ θ ON Sh2 AND VALUE OF
SINH θ (1 TO 10) ON D.

Sh1 = θ (0.1 TO 0.9). READ θ ON Sh1 AND VALUE OF
SINH θ (0.1 TO 1) ON D.

LOG LOG DUPLEX VECTOR SLIDE RULE
(KEUFFEL & ESSER CO #4083-3)

LOG LOG DUPLEX VECTOR SLIDE RULE

SAMPLE SETTINGS

MULTIPLICATION, DIVISION, POWERS, ROOTS, AND LOGARITHMS

Scales A, B, C, D, CI, K, and L same as regular polyphase slide rule. See pp. 3-52 and plate p. 55.

MULTIPLICATION AND DIVISION OF NUMBERS CONTAINING THE FACTOR π

The DF scale known as the "folded" scale contains the factor π.

Multiply 2.62 by π.

On front of rule set hairline of runner to 2.62 on D.

On front of rule on DF, under hairline read 8.23.

Divide 82 by π.

On front of rule set hairline of runner to 82 on DF.

On front of rule on D, under hairline read 26.1.

Find the area of a circle whose diameter is $2\frac{1}{4}''$. Use formula $A = \pi r^2$, $r = 1.125''$.

On front of rule multiply 1.125 by 1.125 and get $1.266 = r^2$.

On front of rule set hairline of runner to 1.266 on D.

On front of rule on DF read 3.98 square inches.

LOG LOG DUPLEX VECTOR SLIDE RULE
CONTINUED ON PAGE 77

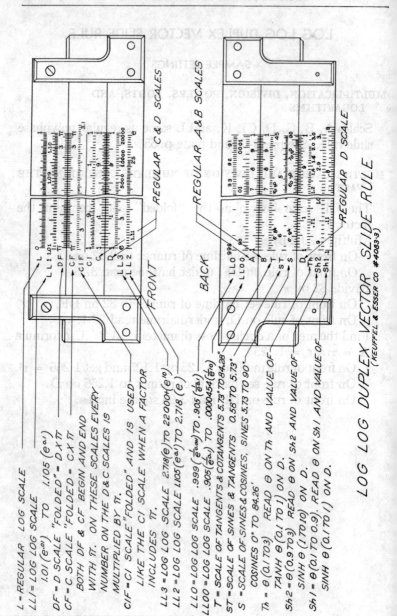

LOG LOG DUPLEX VECTOR SLIDE RULE
(KEUFFEL & ESSER CO #4083-3)

L = REGULAR LOG SCALE

LL1 = LOG LOG SCALE

$1.01\,(e^{.01})$ TO $1.105\,(e^{0.1})$

DF = D SCALE "FOLDED" = $D \times \pi$

CF = C SCALE "FOLDED" = $C \times \pi$

BOTH DF & CF BEGIN AND END
WITH π. ON THESE SCALES EVERY
NUMBER ON THE D & C SCALES IS
MULTIPLIED BY π.

CIF = CI SCALE "FOLDED" AND IS USED
LIKE THE CI SCALE WHEN A FACTOR
INCLUDES π.

LL3 = LOG LOG SCALE $2.718\,(e)$ TO $22000\,(e^{10})$

LL2 = LOG LOG SCALE $1.105\,(e^{0.1})$ TO $2.718\,(e)$

LL0 = LOG LOG SCALE $.999\,(e^{.001})$ TO $.905\,(e^{.1})$

LL00 = LOG LOG SCALE $.905\,(e^{.1})$ TO $.0000454\,(e^{-10})$

T = SCALE OF TANGENTS & COTANGENTS $5.73°$ TO $84.26°$

ST = SCALE OF SINES & TANGENTS $0.58°$ TO $5.73°$

S = SCALE OF SINES & COSINES. SINES 5.73 TO $90°$
COSINES $0°$ TO $84.26'$

Th = $\theta\ (0.1\ TO\ 3)$ READ θ ON Th AND VALUE OF
TANH $\theta\ (0.1\ TO\ 1)$ ON D.

Sh2 = $\theta\ (0.9\ TO\ 3)$ READ θ ON Sh2 AND VALUE OF
SINH $\theta\ (1\ TO\ 10)$ ON D.

Sh1 = $\theta\ (0.1\ TO\ 0.9)$. READ θ ON Sh1 AND VALUE OF
SINH $\theta\ (0.1\ TO\ 1)$ ON D.

REGULAR C & D SCALES

REGULAR A & B SCALES

REGULAR D SCALE

FRONT

BACK

LOG LOG DUPLEX VECTOR SLIDE RULE—Continued

TANGENTS AND COTANGENTS

Find tangent of 10° 40′.

On back of rule set hairline of runner to 10° 40′ (black figures) on T.

On back of rule on D, under hairline read 0.1883.

Find tangent of 80° 20′.

On back of rule set hairline of runner to 80° 20′ (red figures) on T.

On back of rule on DI (red figures) under hairline read 5.87.

Find cotangent of 10° 40′.

On back of rule set hairline of runner to 10° 40′ (black figures) on T.

On back of rule on DI (red figures) under hairline read 5.31.

Find cotangent of 80° 20′.

On back of rule set hairline of runner to 80° 20′ (red figures) on T.

On back of rule on D, under hairline read 0.1703.

SMALL ANGLES TANGENTS AND COTANGENTS

Find tangent of 2° 30′.

On back of rule set hairline of runner to 2° 30′ on ST.

On back of rule on D, under hairline read 0.0437.

Cotangent will be on DI (red figures) = 22.9.

SINES AND COSINES

Find sine of 36° 30′.

On back of rule set hairline of runner to 36° 30′ (black figures) on S.

On back of rule on D, under hairline read 0.595.

Find cosine of 66° 30′.

On back of rule set hairline of runner to 66° 30′ (red figures) on S.

On back of rule on D, under hairline read 0.399.

LOG LOG DUPLEX VECTOR SLIDE RULE
CONTINUED ON PAGE 79

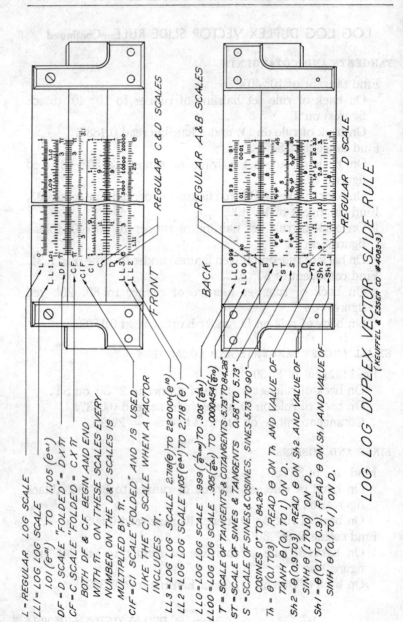

L = REGULAR LOG SCALE

LLI = LOG LOG SCALE
1.01 ($e^{.01}$) TO 1.105 ($e^{.1}$)

DF = D SCALE "FOLDED" = D × π
CF = C SCALE "FOLDED" = C × π
BOTH DF & CF BEGIN AND END
WITH π. ON THESE SCALES EVERY
NUMBER ON THE D&C SCALES IS
MULTIPLIED BY π.

CIF = CI SCALE "FOLDED" AND IS USED
LIKE THE CI SCALE WHEN A FACTOR
INCLUDES π.

LL3 = LOG LOG SCALE 2.718(e^1) TO 22000(e^{10})
LL2 = LOG LOG SCALE 1.105($e^{.1}$) TO 2.718 (e)

LL0 = LOG LOG SCALE .999 ($e^{-.001}$) TO .905 ($e^{-.1}$)
LL00 = LOG LOG SCALE .905 ($e^{-.1}$) TO .0000454 (e^{-10})

T = SCALE OF TANGENTS & COTANGENTS 5.73° TO 84.28°
ST = SCALE OF SINES & TANGENTS 0.58° TO 5.73°
S = SCALE OF SINES & COSINES, SINES 5.73 TO 90°
COSINES 0° TO 84.26°

Th = θ (0.1 TO 3) READ θ ON Th AND VALUE OF
TANH θ (0.1 TO 1) ON D.

Sh2 = θ (0.9703) READ θ ON Sh2 AND VALUE OF
SINH θ (1 TO 10) ON D.

Sh1 = θ (0.1 TO 0.9). READ θ ON Sh1 AND VALUE OF
SINH θ (0.1 TO 1) ON D.

FRONT — REGULAR C & D SCALES

BACK — REGULAR A & B SCALES

REGULAR D SCALE

LOG LOG DUPLEX VECTOR SLIDE RULE
(KEUFFEL & ESSER CO #4083-3)

LOG LOG DUPLEX VECTOR SLIDE RULE—Continued

SMALL ANGLES SINES AND COSINES

Find sine of 2° 30′.

    On back of rule set hairline of runner to 2° 30′ on ST.

    On back of rule on D, under hairline read 0.0436.

    Cosines of small angles on this scale are practically 1 (0.99995 for 35′ and 0.99511 for 5° 40′).

RIGHT TRIANGLES AND COMPLEX QUANTITIES AS $Z = R \pm jX$

Find hypotenuse when base = 4, altitude = 3.

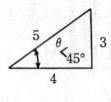

    Set right index of S to 4 on D.

    Over 3 on D read 36.9° (black) on T (means 4 × tan 36.9° = 3 or 4 × $\frac{3}{4}$ = 3).

    Next bring 36.9° (black) on S to 3 on D and under right index of S read 5 on D (means 3 ÷ sin 36.9° = 5 or 3 ÷ $\frac{3}{5}$ = 5).

Use   Black S
          Black T

Find hypotenuse when base = 3, altitude = 4.

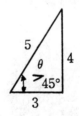

    Set right index of S to 4 on D.

    Over 3 on D read 53.13° (red) on T (means 4 × cot 53.13° = 3 or 4 × $\frac{3}{4}$ = 3).

    Next bring 53.13° (red) on S to 3 on D and under right index of S read 5 on D (means 3 ÷ cot 53.13° = 5 or 3 ÷ $\frac{3}{5}$ = 5).

Use   Red S = cos
          Red T = cot

LOG LOG DUPLEX VECTOR SLIDE RULE
CONTINUED ON PAGE 81

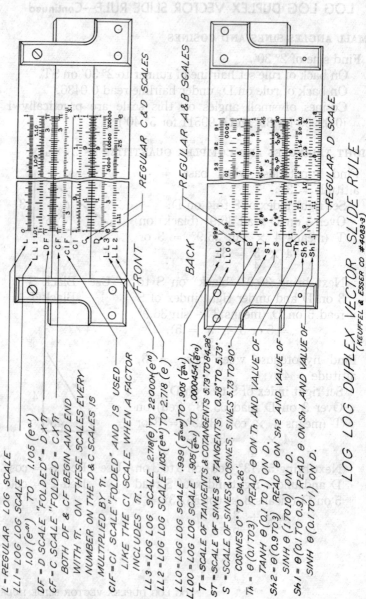

FRONT

REGULAR C & D SCALES

BACK

REGULAR A & B SCALES

REGULAR D SCALE

LOG LOG DUPLEX VECTOR SLIDE RULE
(KEUFFEL & ESSER CO #4083-3)

L = REGULAR LOG SCALE

LLI = LOG LOG SCALE
1.01 $(e^{.01})$ TO 1.105 $(e^{.1})$

DF = D SCALE "FOLDED" = D x π

CF = C SCALE "FOLDED" = C x π

BOTH DF & CF BEGIN AND END
WITH π. ON THESE SCALES EVERY
NUMBER ON THE D&C SCALES IS
MULTIPLIED BY π.

CIF = CI SCALE "FOLDED" AND IS USED
LIKE THE CI SCALE WHEN A FACTOR
INCLUDES π.

LL3 = LOG LOG SCALE 2.718(e) TO 22000(e^{10})

LL2 = LOG LOG SCALE 1.105$(e^{.1})$ TO 2.718 (e)

LLO = LOG LOG SCALE .999 $(e^{-.001}_{.000})$ TO .905 $(e^{-.1}_{.00})$

LLOO = LOG LOG SCALE .905 $(e^{-.1}_{.00})$ TO .0000454(e^{-10}_{0})

T = SCALE OF TANGENTS & COTANGENTS 5.73° TO 84.28°

ST = SCALE OF SINES & TANGENTS 0.58° TO 5.73°

S = SCALE OF SINES & COSINES. SINES 5.73 TO 90°
COSINES 0° TO 84.26°

Th = θ (0.1 TO 3) READ θ ON Th AND VALUE OF

TANH θ (0.1 TO 1) ON D.

Sh2 = θ (0.9 TO 3) READ θ ON Sh2 AND VALUE OF

SINH θ (1 TO 10) ON D.

Sh1 = θ (0.1 TO 0.9). READ θ ON Sh1 AND VALUE OF

SINH θ (0.1 TO 1) ON D.

LOG LOG DUPLEX VECTOR SLIDE RULE—Continued

HYPERBOLIC FUNCTIONS

Th = θ (0.1 to 3). Scale D gives value of tanh θ (0.1 to 1). Thus, tanh 0.224, where θ = 0.224 radians on Th, gives value of tanh 0.224 = 0.222 on D. Tanh 1.45 on Th gives 0.895 on D. For values of θ above 3, tanh θ = 1 approximately.

Sh2 = θ (0.9 to 3). Scale D gives values of sinh θ (1 to 10). Thus, sinh 1.465, where θ = 1.465 radians on Sh2, gives value of sinh 1.465 = 2.05 on D. Sinh 2.95 on Sh2 gives 9.53 on D.

Sh1 = θ (0.1 to 0.9). Scale D gives values of sinh θ (0.1 to 1). Thus, sinh 0.645, where θ = 0.645 radians on Sh1, gives value of sinh 0.645 = 0.69 on D. Sinh 0.273 on Sh1 gives 0.276 on D.

LOG LOG SCALES

LL1 1.01($\epsilon^{0.01}$) TO 1.105($\epsilon^{0.1}$)

Find log of 1.02 to base ϵ.
Set indexes to zero.
Set runner to 1.02 on LL1.
Under hairline of runner on C read logϵ 1.02 = 0.0198.
On LL1 the decimal point will be .0L, thus 0.0198 (see sketch p. 83).

Find 1.02^2.
Set 1 on C to 1.02 on LL1.
Bring runner to power 2 on C.
Under hairline of runner read 1.0404 on LL1.

Find $\sqrt[3]{1.065}$.
Set runner to 1.065 on LL1.
Bring root 3 on C to hairline of runner.
Opposite 1 on C read 1.0212 on LL1.

LOG LOG DUPLEX VECTOR SLIDE RULE
CONTINUED ON PAGE 83

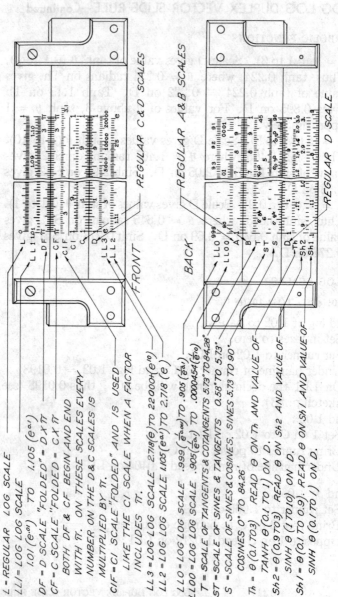

L = REGULAR LOG SCALE

LL1 = LOG LOG SCALE

1.01 ($e^{.01}$)   TO   1.105 ($e^{0.1}$)

DF = D SCALE "FOLDED" = $D \times \pi$

CF = C SCALE "FOLDED" = $C \times \pi$

BOTH DF & CF BEGIN AND END
WITH π. ON THESE SCALES THE
NUMBER ON THE D & C SCALES IS
MULTIPLIED BY π.

CIF = CI SCALE "FOLDED" AND IS USED
LIKE THE CI SCALE WHEN A FACTOR
INCLUDES π.

LL3 = LOG LOG SCALE 2.718 (e) TO 22000 (e^{10})

LL2 = LOG LOG SCALE 1.105 ($e^{0.1}$) TO 2.718 (e)

LL0 = LOG LOG SCALE .999 ($e^{-.001}$) TO .905 ($\frac{1}{e^{.1}}$)

LL00 = LOG LOG SCALE .905 ($\frac{1}{e^{.1}}$) TO .0000454 ($\frac{1}{e^{10}}$)

T = SCALE OF TANGENTS & COTANGENTS 5.73° TO 84.28°

ST = SCALE OF SINES & TANGENTS 0.58° TO 5.73°

S = SCALE OF SINES & COSINES, SINES 5.73 TO 90°
COSINES 0° TO 84.26°

Th = θ (0.1 TO 3)   READ θ ON Th AND VALUE OF
TANH θ (0.1 TO 1) ON D.

Sh2 = θ (0.9 TO 3) READ θ ON Sh2 AND VALUE OF
SINH θ (1 TO 10) ON D.

Sh1 = θ (0.1 TO 0.9) READ θ ON Sh1 AND VALUE OF
SINH θ (0.1 TO 1) ON D.

REGULAR C & D SCALES

REGULAR A & B SCALES

REGULAR D SCALE

FRONT

BACK

LOG LOG DUPLEX VECTOR SLIDE RULE
(KEUFFEL & ESSER CO #4083-3)

LOG LOG DUPLEX VECTOR SLIDE RULE—Continued

LL2 $1.105(\epsilon^{0.1})$ **TO** $2.718(\epsilon^{1})$

Find log of 1.25 to base ϵ.

Set indexes to zero.

Set runner to 1.25 on LL2.

Under hairline of runner on C, read $\log_\epsilon 1.25 = 0.223$.

On LL2 the decimal point will be 0.L, thus 0.223 (see sketch).

Find $1.16^{3.4}$.

Set 1 on C to 1.16 on LL2.

Bring runner to power 3.4 on C.

Under hairline of runner read 1.656 on LL2.

Find $\sqrt[2.4]{2.1}$.

Set runner to 2.1 on LL2.

Bring root 2.4 on C to hairline of runner.

Opposite 1 on C read 1.362 on LL2.

LL3 $2.718(\epsilon)$ **TO** $22000+(\epsilon^{10})$

Find log of 10 to base ϵ.

Set indexes to zero.

Set runner to 10 on LL3.

Under hairline of runner on C, read $\log_\epsilon 10 = 2.3$

On LL3 the decimal point will be L., thus 2.3 (see sketch).

Find 15.3^2.

Set 1 on C to 15.3 on LL3.

Bring runner to power 2 on C.

Under hairline of runner read 234 on LL3.

Find $\sqrt[3.2]{68}$.

Set runner to 68 on LL3.

Bring root 3.2 on C to hairline of runner.

Opposite 1 on C, read 3.74 on LL3.

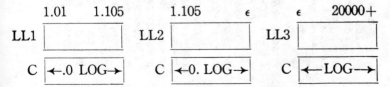

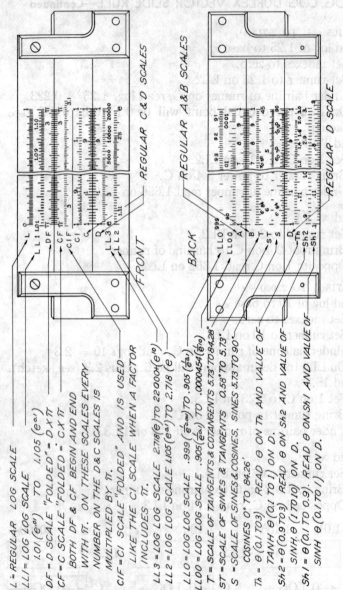

L = REGULAR LOG SCALE
LLI = LOG LOG SCALE
     1.01 ($e^{.01}$) TO 1.105 ($e^{.1}$)
DF = D SCALE "FOLDED" = D × π
CF = C SCALE "FOLDED" = C × π
     BOTH D & C BEGIN AND END
     WITH π. ON THESE SCALES EVERY
     NUMBER ON THE D & C SCALES IS
     MULTIPLIED BY π.
CIF = CI SCALE "FOLDED" AND IS USED
     LIKE THE CI SCALE WHEN A FACTOR
     INCLUDES, π.
LL3 = LOG LOG SCALE 2.718 (e) TO 22000 (e^{10})
LL2 = LOG LOG SCALE 1.105 ($e^{.1}$) TO 2.718 (e)

LLO = LOG LOG SCALE .999 ($\frac{1}{e^{.001}}$) TO .905 ($\frac{1}{e^{.1}}$)
LLOO = LOG LOG SCALE .905 ($\frac{1}{e^{.1}}$) TO .0000454 ($\frac{1}{e^{10}}$)
T = SCALE OF TANGENTS & COTANGENTS 5.73° TO 84.28°
ST = SCALE OF SINES & TANGENTS 0.58° TO 5.73°
S = SCALE OF SINES & COSINES, SINES 5.73 TO 90°
     COSINES 0° TO 84.26°
Th = θ (0.1 TO 3) READ θ ON Th AND VALUE OF
     TANH θ (0.1 TO 1) ON D.
Sh2 = θ (0.9 TO 3) READ θ ON Sh2 AND VALUE OF
     SINH θ (1 TO 10) ON D.
Sh1 = θ (0.1 TO 0.9). READ θ ON Sh1 AND VALUE OF
     SINH θ (0.1 TO 1) ON D.

LOG LOG DUPLEX VECTOR SLIDE RULE
(KEUFFEL & ESSER CO #4083-3)

LOG LOG DUPLEX VECTOR SLIDE RULE—Continued

$$\text{LL0} \ \ .999 \ \ \left(\frac{1}{\epsilon^{0\cdot001}}\right) \quad \text{TO} \ \ .905 \ \ \left(\frac{1}{\epsilon^{0\cdot1}}\right)$$

The LL0 scale is used with the A (or B) scale. Numbers on the LL0 scale have their cologarithms to the base ϵ on the A or B scale.

Find log of 0.995 to the base ϵ.

Set runner to .995 on LL0.

Under hairline of runner read 0.005 on A.

0.005 is the colog. of 0.995 to the base ϵ.

So $\log_\epsilon 0.995 = (10 - 10) - 0.005 = 9.995 - 10$.

On LL0 .999 to .99 the decimal point is .00 colog, thus 0.005 (see sketch p. 87).

Find log 0.94 to the base ϵ.

Set runner to .94 on LL0.

Under hairline of runner read 0.062 on A.

.062 is the colog. of 0.94 to the base ϵ.

So $\log_\epsilon 0.94 = (10 - 10) - 0.062 = 9.938 - 10$.

On LL0 .99 to .905 the decimal point is .0 colog, thus 0.062 (see sketch p. 87).

Find $0.92^{1.6}$.

Set 1 on B to .92 on LL0.

Bring runner to power 1.6 on B.

Under hairline of runner read 0.8751 on LL0.

Find $\sqrt[3.2]{0.96}$.

Set runner to .96 on LL0.

Bring root 3.2 on B to hairline of runner.

Opposite 1 on B read 0.9873 on LL0.

LOG LOG DUPLEX VECTOR SLIDE RULE
CONTINUED ON PAGE 87

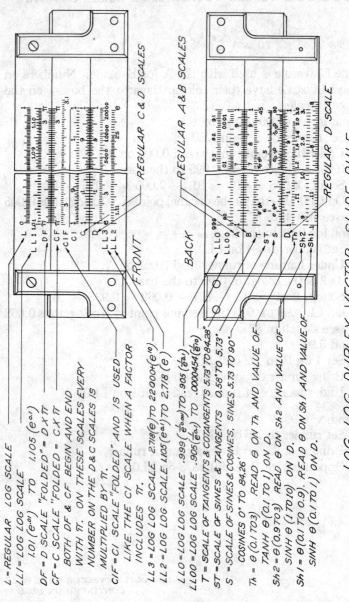

LOG LOG DUPLEX VECTOR SLIDE RULE
(KEUFFEL & ESSER CO #4083-3)

L = REGULAR LOG SCALE

LLI = LOG LOG SCALE
1.01 $(e^{.01})$ TO 1.105 $(e^{.1})$

DF = D SCALE "FOLDED" = D x π
CF = C SCALE "FOLDED" = C x π

BOTH DF & CF BEGIN AND END
WITH π. ON THESE SCALES EVERY
NUMBER ON THE D&C SCALES IS
MULTIPLIED BY π.

CIF = CI SCALE "FOLDED" AND IS USED
LIKE THE CI SCALE WHEN A FACTOR
INCLUDES π.

LL3 = LOG LOG SCALE 2.718 $(e^{1.0})$ TO 22000 (e^{10})
LL2 = LOG LOG SCALE 1.105 $(e^{0.1})$ TO 2.718 (e)

LL0 = LOG LOG SCALE .999 $(e^{-.001})$ TO .905 $(e^{-.1})$
LL00 = LOG LOG SCALE .905 $(e^{-.1})$ TO .000454 $(e^{-7.0})$

T = SCALE OF TANGENTS & COTANGENTS 5.73° TO 84.28°
ST = SCALE OF SINES & TANGENTS 0.58° TO 5.73°
S = SCALE OF SINES & COSINES, SINES 5.73 TO 90°
COSINES 0° TO 84.26°

Th = θ (0.1 TO 3) READ θ ON Th AND VALUE OF
TANH θ (0.1 TO 1) ON D.
Sh2 = θ (0.9 TO 3) READ θ ON Sh2 AND VALUE OF
SINH θ (1 TO 10) ON D.
Sh1 = θ (0.1 TO 0.9) READ θ ON Sh1 AND VALUE OF
SINH θ (0.1 TO 1) ON D.

— REGULAR C & D SCALES

REGULAR A & B SCALES

REGULAR D SCALE

FRONT

BACK

LOG LOG DUPLEX VECTOR SLIDE RULE—Continued

LL00 .905 $\left(\dfrac{1}{\epsilon^{0.1}}\right)$ TO .000454 $\left(\dfrac{1}{\epsilon^{10}}\right)$

The LL00 scale is used with the A (or B) scale. Numbers on the LL00 scale have their cologarithms to the base ϵ on the A or B scale.

Find log 0.8 to the base ϵ.

Set runner to .8 on LL00.

Under hairline of runner read 0.223 on A.

0.223 is the colog. of 0.8 to the base ϵ.

So $\log_\epsilon$ 0.8 = (10 − 10) − 0.223 = 9.777 − 10.

On LL00 .905 to .37 the decimal point is .colog, thus 0.223 (see sketch).

Find $\log_\epsilon$ 0.05.

Set runner to 0.05 on LL00.

Under hairline of runner read 3 on A.

3 is the colog. of 0.05 to the base ϵ.

So $\log_\epsilon$ 0.05 = (10 − 10) − 3 = 7.00 − 10.

On LL00 .37 to .000454 the decimal point is colog., thus 3. (see sketch).

Find $0.075^{1.4}$.

Set 1 on A to .075 on LL00.

Bring runner to power 1.4 on A.

Under hairline of runner read 0.0266 on LL00.

Find $\sqrt[3.7]{0.14}$.

Set runner to .14 on LL00.

Bring root 3.7 on B to hairline of runner.

Opposite 1 on B read 0.588 on LL00.

	.999	.99	.905		.905	.37	.000454
LL0				LL00			
A	←.00 colog→	←.0 colog→		A	←. colog→	←colog .→	

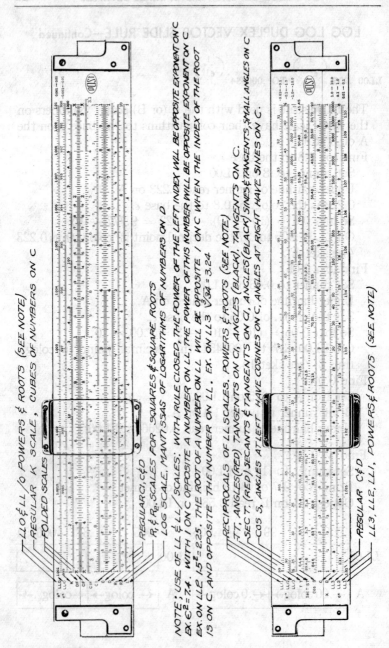

NOTE: USE OF LL & LL/ SCALES: WITH RULE CLOSED, THE POWER OF THE LEFT INDEX WILL BE OPPOSITE EXPONENT ON C. EX: $e^2 = 7.4$. WITH 1 ON C OPPOSITE A NUMBER ON LL, THE POWER OF THIS NUMBER WILL BE OPPOSITE EXPONENT ON C. EX: ON LL2 $1.5^2 = 2.25$. THE ROOT OF A NUMBER ON LL WILL BE OPPOSITE 1 ON C WHEN THE INDEX OF THE ROOT IS ON C AND OPPOSITE THE NUMBER ON LL. EX: ON LL3 $\sqrt[3]{34} = 3.24$

Fig. 30.

POST VERSALOG SLIDE RULE

The 23 scales of the Versalog slide rule include the scales usually found on slide rules and special scales which facilitate scientific and engineering computations. The scales common to most rules (see Fig. 30 for their location) have been explained on the following pages: C, p. *4*; D, p. *4*; CI, pp. *6, 8, 9*; CF and DF, pp. *22-25;* K, p. *35;* and L, pp. *7, 48-52*. The CIF scale is an "inverted" CF scale.

The front of the rule has two scales (R_1 and R_2) for squaring numbers or extracting their square roots. These scales are used with the D scale. Thus, if the hairline of the runner is brought to 2 on R_1, the square of 2 (which is 4) will be found on D. Similarly, 6.4 on R_2 will have its square (41) on D. Conversely, a number found on D will have its square root on R_1 or R_2. Thus, 9 on D has its square root, 3, on R_1; 64 on D has its square root, 8, on R_2.

SQUARE ROOT

If the span (p. *12*) is even (the notation of this book being used), the square root of a number on the D scale will be on the R scale with the even subscript. For example,

$\sqrt{90}$, span = 2 (even) under 90 on D find 9.49 on R_2.

$\sqrt{9}$, span = 1 (odd) under 9 on D find 3 on R_1.

This method applies equally well to decimal fractions. For example,

$\sqrt{.0005}$, span − 3 (odd). The square root is .02236, and the span of .02236 = − 1 (odd) found on R_1.

$\sqrt{.005}$, span −2, even, and the square root is .0707 on R_2.

The methods described on pages 30-34 may be used if preferred.)

SQUARING

The square of a number on R_1 will have a span that is odd. Thus, 250 is on R_1 and its span, 3, is odd. Its square, 62,500, whose span is odd, will be found on D. Similarly, 52 whose span is 2, and even, will have 2,700 as its square and an even span of 4.

LOG LOG SCALES

Note that six of the eight scales marked LL are on the back of the rule (Fig. 30).

The log log scale gives the logarithms of logarithms. It is useful in finding values of $\epsilon^x (2.718)^x$ quickly, in raising numbers to integral or fractional powers, and in extracting integral or fractional roots. The Versalog slide rule has eight log log scales ranging from 1.001 to 22,000 and from 0.00005 to 0.999.

The LL3 scale will be used to explain the theory and application of the log log scales. Scale LL3 starts at ϵ (Epsilon) whose value is 2.718, and it extends to 20,000. This scale and all other log log scales are used with the C and D scales. Manipulation of the LL3, C, and D scales will give powers and roots of numbers from 2.718 to 22,000. The other seven scales are used for numbers below 2.718.

An example will show how to raise (2.718) to the 5th power. The left index of D is directly over 2.718 on LL3. To raise 2.718 to the 5th power, it is necessary only to move the runner to the right so that the hairline is over 5 on D. The 5th power of 2.718 will be found on LL3 under the hairline and is 150.

To raise 4 to the 3.32 power, set the left index of C over 4 on LL3. Move the hairline of the runner to 3.32 on C. Under the hairline find 159 on LL3, the 3.32 power of 4. This setting eliminates the rather slow process:

$$Log_{10} 4 = 0.602$$
$$3.32 \text{ x } log_{10} 4 = 3.32 \text{ x } .602 = 2$$
$$antilog\ 2 = 159.$$

To find

$$\sqrt[2.26]{50},$$ bring the hairline to 50 on LL3.

Bring 2.26 on C to the hairline. Under 1 on C find 5.65 on LL3 which is the 2.26 root of 50.

Checking arithmetically, $log_{10} 50 = 1.699$ (from a table)

$$\frac{1.699}{2.26} = .0752 \qquad antilog\ 0.752 = 5.65$$

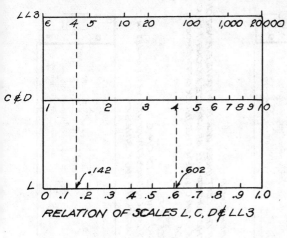

Fig. 31.

The relations of the scales just used will be clear from Fig. 31.

The LL3 scale is divided in proportion to $\log_{10}(\log \epsilon\ N)$ where N is a number ranging from 2.718 to 20,000.

Ex.: N = 4, 4 on LL3 is opposite 0.142 on L which is the $\log_{10}(\log \epsilon\ 4)$ or $\log_{10}(1.386) = 0.142$. (1.386 is obtained from a table of logarithms to the base ϵ known as a Table of Natural Logarithms.)

The C and D scales are divided logarithmically into 10 parts from 1 to 10. The logarithm of a number on C or D will be found on Scale L. Ex.: $\log_{10} 4 = 0.602$.

The L or log scale is divided into 10 equal parts, with numbering from 0 to 1. A number on this scale is the mantissa of the logarithm of the number above it on C or D.

METHOD OF USING LOG LOG SCALES

LL3 (2.718) 20,000

Using the method in the preceding examples, verify the following:

$$15.5^{3.1} = 4,898$$
$$\sqrt[1.5]{500} = 63$$

LL2   1.105 . . . . ϵ (2.718)

Raise 1.3 to the 2.54 power.

Move the left-hand index on C to 1.3 on LL2. Under

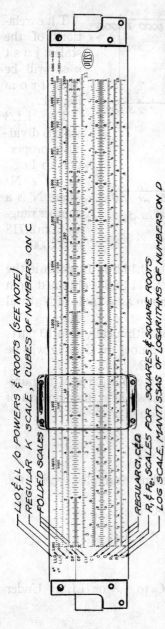

LL0 & L/0 POWERS & ROOTS (SEE NOTE)

REGULAR K SCALE, CUBES OF NUMBERS ON C

R, & Re, SCALES FOR SQUARES & SQUARE ROOTS

LOG SCALE, MANTISSAS OF LOGARITHMS OF NUMBERS ON D

FOLDED SCALES

REGULAR C & D

NOTE: USE OF LL & LL/ SCALES: WITH RULE CLOSED, THE POWER OF THE LEFT INDEX WILL BE OPPOSITE EXPONENT ON C
EX. $e^2 = 7.4$. WITH I ON C OPPOSITE A NUMBER ON LL, THE POWER OF THIS NUMBER WILL BE OPPOSITE EXPONENT ON C
EX. ON LL2 $1.5^2 = 2.25$. THE ROOT OF A NUMBER ON LL WILL BE OPPOSITE I ON C WHEN THE INDEX OF THE ROOT
IS ON C AND OPPOSITE THE NUMBER ON LL. EX. ON LL3 $\sqrt[3]{34} = 3.24$.

RECIPROCALS OF LL SCALES, POWERS & ROOTS (SEE NOTE)

T T, ANGLES (RED) TANGENTS ON CI, ANGLES (BLACK) TANGENTS ON C.

SEC T. (RED) SECANTS & TANGENTS ON CI, ANGLES (BLACK) SINES & TANGENTS, SMALL ANGLES ON C

COS S, ANGLES AT LEFT HAVE COSINES ON C, ANGLES AT RIGHT HAVE SINES ON C.

REGULAR C & D

LL3, LL2, LL1, POWERS & ROOTS (SEE NOTE)

2.54 on C read 1.95 on LL2.

$\sqrt[2.9]{1.5}$ = Hairline to 1.5 on LL2.   2.9 on C to hairline.
Under left-hand index of C read 1.15 on LL2.

LL1   1.01...............1.105

1.02^2 Hairline to 1.02 on LL1.   Left-hand index of C to
hairline.   Under 2 on C read 1.0404 on LL1.

LL0   1.001...........1.01

1.003$^{1.2}$ Hairline to 1.003 on LL0.   Left-hand index of C
to hairline.   Over 1.2 on C read 1.0036 on LL0.

The scales	LL/3	.367	.00005
	LL/2	.905	.367
	LL/1	.99	.905
	LL/0	.999	.990

are known as reciprocal log log scales since the numbers on
them are reciprocals of those on LL3, LL2, LL1, and LL0.

Ex.: 0.92^2

.92 is on the LL/1 scale.   Hairline to .92 on LL/1.

Right-hand index of C to hairline.   Over 2 on C, read .846
on LL/1.

TRIGONOMETRIC SCALES

Three trigonometric scales are located on the slide.   Each
has a double marking giving the equivalent of six scales.   These
scales are used with the C scale and the CI scale.   Two of the
three scales are marked in black and red.   A black marking
is always used with the C scale which is black.   A red marking
is always used with the CI scale which is red.   These scales
enable one to find the sine, cosine, tangent, and secant easily
and quickly.

TANGENTS

The upper scale is for tangents and is marked TT.   The
left-hand T is red and the right-hand T is black.   The following
examples will illustrate the use of the scale.

Find the tangent of 20°.   With the rule closed, find 20 near
the center of the TT scale and bring the hairline to it.   Since
20 is in black, the C scale will be used to find the tangent.

Under the hairline, find 0.364 on Scale C. 0.364 is the tangent of 20°.

Find the tangent of 80°. Bring the hairline to the red 80 near the left-hand end of Scale TT. On the reverse side, find 5.67 under the hairline on CI. 5.67 is the tangent of 80°.

SECANTS, SINES, AND TANGENTS

The center scale is for secants and for the sines and tangents of small angles. (The sines and tangents of small angles are practically the same.) The scale is marked at the left-hand end Sec T ST. Sec T is in red; ST, in black.

Ex.: Find the secant of 86°. With the rule closed, bring the hairline to the red 86 which is near the right-hand end of the scale. On the reverse side of the rule, find 14.3 under the hairline on Scale CI. 14.3 is the secant of 86°. Examination of a table of trigonometric functions will show that the secant and tangent are practically the same for the angles marked in red on the Sec T scale.

Ex.: Find the tangent of 1.5°. Bring the hairline to the black 1.5. On Scale C find 0.0262 under the hairline. 0.0262 is the tangent of 1.5°. Find the sine of 2°. Bring the hairline to the black 2 on ST scale. Under the hairline find .0349 on Scale C. .0349 is the tangent of 2°.

COSINES AND SINES

The lower scale is for cosines and for the sines of angles larger than those given by scale ST. The marking Cos S at the left-hand end of the rule means that with the double marking on this rule, the scale gives the cosine of an angle at the left of a graduation and the sine of an angle at the right of a graduation. Since all angles are in black, Scale C is used.

Ex.: Find the cosine of 70°. With the rule closed, find 70 near the center of the rule. 70 is at the left of a graduation, so the scale will give its cosine. Bring the hairline to 70. Under the hairline, find 0.342 on Scale C. 0.342 is the cosine of 70°.

Ex.: Find the sine of 30°. Bring the hairline to 30 on the right-hand side of the marking 60⊥30. Since 30 is at the right of a graduation, the scale will give its sine. Under the hairline read 0.5 on C. 0.5 is the sine of 30°. The sine of 30 is of the same value as the cosine of 60 (its complement). This is in accordance with the marking of the scale.

RIGHT TRIANGLES AND VECTORS

Two triangles will be used as examples.

Ex.: Find the sine and cosine of the angle included between the hypotenuse, c = 2, and the long side, 1.73, in the triangle whose sides are: c = 2, b = 1.732 and a = 1.

First find the angle whose cosine is $\dfrac{1.732}{2}$ = .866. With the rule closed bring the hairline to .866 on C. Under the hairline find 30° at the left of 30⊥60 on Cos S. With the rule still closed, bring the hairline to the 30 at the right of 60⊥30 on Cos S. Under the hairline on C, find the sine of 30° which is 0.5.

Vectors are handled in the same manner as right triangles.

Ex.: Find the real component R and the quadrature component jX of the vector Z = 20 which is at 35° with the horizontal component R.

$$\frac{R}{Z} = \cos 35°, \quad \frac{X}{Z} = \sin 35°, \quad R = Z \cos 35°, \quad X = Z \sin 35°$$

The sine of 35°, which will be found under 35° at the right of the graduation 60⊥30, is 0.573. Then X = Z sin 35° = 20 x .573 = 11.46. It is not necessary to read sin 35°. Simply move the slide to the left until 1 on C stands over 20 on D and under 35° on Cos S, read 11.36.

The real component is R = Z cos 35°. Set 1 on C over 20 on D. Under 35 to left of 30⊥60, find 16.4 on D.

We now have 20 /35° = 16.4 + j11.46.

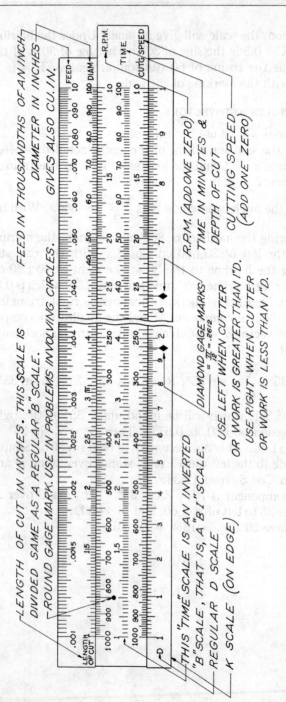

THE LANGSNER INDUSTRIAL SLIDE RULE
(EUGENE DIETZGEN CO.)

LANGSNER INDUSTRIAL SLIDE RULE

SAMPLE SETTINGS

DIAMETER AND R.P.M. GIVEN. TO FIND CUTTING SPEED

Set R.P.M. to diam. over diamond gauge mark. Read CUTTING SPEED.

Ex. At what surface speed is a 20″ grinding wheel running if the spindle turns at 1150 R.P.M.?

Set 1150 (115) on R.P.M. under 20 on DIAM.

Over left diamond gauge mark on D read 6020 (602) ft. per min.

DIAMETER AND CUTTING SPEED GIVEN. TO FIND R.P.M.

Set CUTTING SPEED to diamond gauge mark on D. Under DIAM. read R.P.M.

Ex. Find the R.P.M. of a cutter 2″ in diameter which has a cutting speed of 62.6 ft. per min.

Set 62.6 on CUTTING SPEED to left diamond gauge mark on D.

On R.P.M. scale under 2″ DIAM. read 120 R.P.M.

CUTTING SPEED AND R.P.M. GIVEN. TO FIND DIAMETER

Set CUTTING SPEED to diamond gauge mark on D. Above R.P.M. read DIAM.

Ex. Find the diameter of a grinding wheel that is to make 5100 R.P.M. and have a cutting speed of 6000 ft. per min.

Set 6000 (600) on CUTTING SPEED to left diamond gauge mark on D.

Over 5100 (510) on R.P.M. read 4.5 on DIAM.

LANGSNER INDUSTRIAL SLIDE RULE
CONTINUED ON PAGE 99

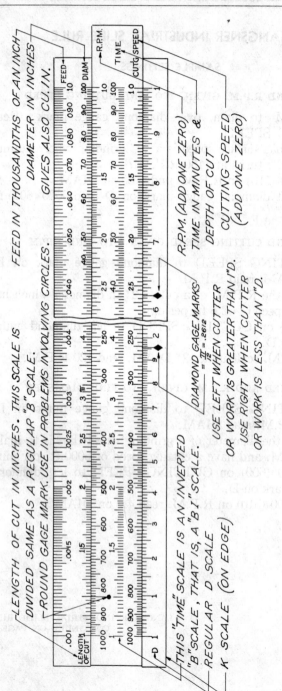

THE LANGSNER INDUSTRIAL SLIDE RULE
(EUGENE DIETZGEN CO.)

LANGSNER INDUSTRIAL SLIDE RULE—Continued

R.P.M., FEED, AND LENGTH OF CUT GIVEN. TO FIND TIME

Set R.P.M. to FEED. Under LENGTH OF CUT find TIME.

Ex. A surface grinder runs at 2000 R.P.M. and has a feed of 0.01″. The length of cut is 4″. How long will it take the wheel to make the 4″ cut?

Set 2000 (200) on R.P.M. to 0.01 on FEED. Move runner to 4 on LENGTH OF CUT.

Under hairline of runner read 2 (0.2) on TIME. So time = 0.2 min.

R.P.M., FEED, AND TIME GIVEN. TO FIND LENGTH OF CUT

Set R.P.M. to FEED. Set runner to TIME and under hairline of runner read LENGTH OF CUT.

Ex. The R.P.M. of a wheel is 2000 and the feed is 0.004″. How far will the wheel grind in 0.25 minutes?

Set 2000 (200) on R.P.M. to 0.004″ on FEED. Move runner to 2.5 (0.25) on TIME.

Under hairline of runner read 2 on LENGTH OF CUT.

R.P.M., TIME, AND LENGTH OF CUT GIVEN. TO FIND FEED

Set TIME to LENGTH OF CUT. Over R.P.M. find FEED.

Ex. If it takes 1½ minutes to drill ⅞″ deep at 185 R.P.M. what will the feed be?

Set 0.5 (5) on TIME to 0.875 (8.75) on LENGTH OF CUT.

Move runner to 185 on R.P.M. and read 0.0095 on FEED.

LANGSNER INDUSTRIAL SLIDE RULE
CONTINUED ON PAGE 101

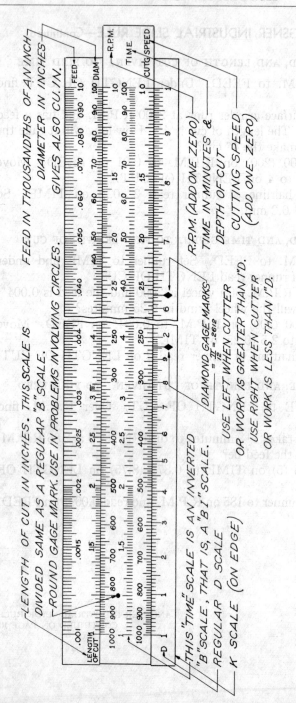

LENGTH OF CUT IN INCHES. THIS SCALE IS
DIVIDED SAME AS A REGULAR "B" SCALE.

ROUND GAGE MARK. USE IN PROBLEMS INVOLVING CIRCLES.

FEED IN THOUSANDTHS OF AN INCH
DIAMETER IN INCHES
GIVES ALSO CU. IN.

R.P.M. (ADD ONE ZERO)
TIME IN MINUTES &
DEPTH OF CUT
CUTTING SPEED
(ADD ONE ZERO)

DIAMOND GAGE MARKS
= $\frac{\pi}{12}$ = .2612

USE LEFT WHEN CUTTER
OR WORK IS GREATER THAN I"D.
USE RIGHT WHEN CUTTER
OR WORK IS LESS THAN I"D.

THIS "TIME" SCALE IS AN INVERTED
"B" SCALE, THAT IS, A "BI" SCALE.

REGULAR "D" SCALE

K SCALE (ON EDGE)

THE LANGSNER INDUSTRIAL SLIDE RULE
(EUGENE DIETZGEN CO.)

LANGSNER INDUSTRIAL SLIDE RULE—Continued

LENGTH OF CUT, FEED, AND TIME GIVEN. TO FIND R.P.M.

Set TIME to LENGTH OF CUT. Under FEED find R.P.M.

Ex. Length of cut 2″, feed 0.016″, time 1.25 minutes. What speed of cutter is required?

    Set 1.25 on TIME to 2″ on LENGTH OF CUT.

    Move runner to 0.016″ on FEED.

    Under hairline of runner read 100 R.P.M. on R.P.M.

Note: Other computations that can be made on the rule with the slide in the position shown by the drawing involve cutting speed, feed, length of cut, and cubic inches of material removed.

When the slide is turned over and inserted in the rule, the rule becomes a regular slide rule with B, CI, C, and D scales. The DIAM. scale is used as an A scale. The rule can then be used to compute costs, change gears, horsepower, indexing, lever arms, load on columns, load on springs, machining time, percentage, and volume. It can also be used for the regular operations of multiplication, division, squares and square roots, cubes and cube roots. Scales for sines, cosines, tangents, cotangents, and logarithms are not on the Langsner Industrial Slide Rule.

APPENDIX

A. PROBLEMS FOR DRILL

MULTIPLICATION

(1) $520 \times 3.5 =$
    $3 + 1 = 4$
(2) $981 \times 0.0043 =$
(3) $0.000166 \times 0.705 =$
(4) $0.0196 \times 0.29 =$
(5) 2560×0.0026
(6) $0.715 \times 0.0137 =$
(7) $2.8 \times 5.1 \times 96 =$
(8) $2.5 \times 605 \times 94 =$
(9) $2.55 \times 3.1416 \times 108 =$
(10) $0.00195 \times 195 \times 350 =$

DIVISION

(1) $\dfrac{387}{55.5} =$
    $3 - 2 = 1$

(2) $\dfrac{115}{4450} =$

(3) $\dfrac{0.00692}{0.00085} =$

(4) $\dfrac{3500}{0.063} =$

(5) $\dfrac{0.008}{852} =$

(6) $\dfrac{955}{852} =$

(7) $\dfrac{0.00760}{0.051} =$

(8) $\dfrac{405}{0.0215} =$

(9) $\dfrac{195}{1800} =$

(10) $\dfrac{0.0409}{161} =$

COMBINED MULTIPLICATION AND DIVISION

(1) $$\frac{160 \times 75}{28.5 \times 22_R} =$$

$$3 - 2 + 2 - 2 + 1 = 6$$
$$\frac{4}{2}$$

(2) $$\frac{156 \times 3.36}{72.5 \times 12.8} =$$

(3) $$\frac{550 \times 82}{20 \times 22} =$$

(4) $$\frac{0.008 \times 3}{0.012 \times 6} =$$

(5) $$\frac{143.5 \times 2.3 \times 2}{82 \times 56} =$$

(6) $$\frac{0.0063 \times 0.0495}{0.000012 \times 18} =$$

(7) $$\frac{160 \times 54 \times 0.0092}{92.8 \times 45 \times 0.986} =$$

(8) $$\frac{360 \times 458 \times 95}{92 \times 13 \times 0.00012} =$$

(9) $$\frac{20}{375 \times 0.065 \times 980} =$$

(10) $$\frac{0.000655}{41 \times 80 \times 35} =$$

RECIPROCALS

Check by regular division using C and D scales.

(1) $\dfrac{1}{2.8}$ =

(2) $\dfrac{1}{29}$ =

(3) $\dfrac{1}{283.5}$ =

(4) $\dfrac{1}{9580}$ =

(5) $\dfrac{1}{1070}$ =

(6) $\dfrac{1}{0.0625}$ =

(7) $\dfrac{1}{0.0013}$ =

(8) $\dfrac{1}{0.00028}$ =

(9) $\dfrac{1}{0.000092}$ =

(10) $\dfrac{1}{0.00000290}$ =

SQUARING NUMBERS

Check by regular multiplication using C and D scales.

(1) 3.8^2 =

Right-hand section, 2S = 2

(2) 52.2^2 =

(3) 792^2 =

(4) 0.052^2 =

(5) 0.319^2 =

(6) 2.7^2 =

Left-hand section, 2S − 1 = 1

(7) 21.5^2 =

(8) 175^2 =

(9) 0.0135^2 =

(10) 0.208 =

SQUARE ROOT

(1) $\sqrt{353}$ = \
(2) $\sqrt{1,188}$ = \
(3) $\sqrt{0.00642}$ = \
(4) $\sqrt{0.0054}$ = \
(5) $\sqrt{0.0005}$ = \
(6) $\sqrt{0.006}$ = \
(7) $\sqrt{0.08176}$ = \
(8) $\sqrt{20,900}$ = \
(9) $\sqrt{960,000}$ = \
(10) $\sqrt{10,026}$ =

CUBING NUMBERS

(1) 6.1^3 = \
Third section, 3S = 3 \
(2) 0.75^3 = \
(3) 0.052^3 = \
(4) 41^3 = \
Second section, 3S − 1 = 5 \
(5) 0.031^3 = \
(6) 0.22^3 = \
(7) 4.5^3 = \
(8) 11.2^3 = \
First section, 3S − 2 = 4 \
(9) 0.205^3 = \
(10) 1.9^3 =

CUBE ROOT

(1) $\sqrt[3]{151}$ =

(2) $\sqrt[3]{252}$ =

(3) $\sqrt[3]{989}$ =

(4) $\sqrt[3]{98}$ =

(5) $\sqrt[3]{0.020}$ =

(6) $\sqrt[3]{0.09}$ =

(7) $\sqrt[3]{0.310}$ =

(8) $\sqrt[3]{0.031}$ =

(9) $\sqrt[3]{0.0031}$ =

(10) $\sqrt[3]{0.000310}$ =

SINES

(1) $38°$ =

(2) $10.5°$ =

(3) $5° \ 10'$ =

(4) $3°$ =

(5) $2° \ 30'$ =

(6) $40'$ =

(7) $15'$ =

(8) $36'$ =

(9) $12''$ =

(10) $30''$ =

COSINES

(1) 70° =

(2) 50° =

(3) 30° 3′ =

(4) 20° =

(5) 12.5° =

(6) 80° =

(7) 20° 20′ =

(8) 95° =

(9) 150° =

(10) 40° 10′ =

TANGENTS

(1) 43° =

(2) 38.5° =

(3) 23° =

(4) 15° 30′ =

(5) 10° =

(6) 6° =

(7) 3° =

(8) 106° =

(9) 135° =

(10) 170° =

COTANGENTS

(1) $37° =$
(2) $33.5° =$
(3) $24° 10' =$
(4) $17° =$
(5) $10° =$
(6) $6° =$
(7) $140° =$
(8) $70° =$
(9) $280° =$
(10) $190° =$

LOGARITHMS

Find the numbers whose logarithms are the following:

Logarithm
(1) $2.767 =$
(2) $1.987 =$
(3) $0.332 =$
(4) $9.176 - 10 =$
(5) $7.462 - 10 =$

Find the logarithms of the following:

Number
(6) $292 =$
(7) $76.5 =$
(8) $8.8 =$
(9) $0.65 =$
(10) $0.00915 =$

POWERS AND ROOTS

Raise the following to the powers indicated:

(1) $3.2^{2.5} =$
(2) $14.8^{3.1} =$
(3) $252^{1.5} =$
(4) $0.08^{0.5} =$
(5) $0.7^4 =$

Find the roots indicated below:

(6) $\sqrt[3.2]{3950}$ = _____

(7) $\sqrt[5]{762}$ = _____

(8) $\sqrt[0.2]{9}$ = _____

(9) $\sqrt[2.1]{.07}$ = _____

(10) $\sqrt[3]{.006}$ = _____

B. PRACTICAL PROBLEMS

PROBLEMS IN AREAS

Right Triangle

$c = \sqrt{a^2 + b^2}$

$a = \sqrt{c^2 - b^2}$

$b = \sqrt{c^2 - a^2}$

Area $= A = \dfrac{1}{2}ab$

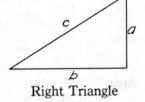

Right Triangle

Slide Rule Problem

(1) $a = 3.5, b = 4.2$

$c = \sqrt{(3.5)^2 + (4.2)^2} = \boxed{}$

$A = \dfrac{1}{2} \times 3.5 \times 4.2 = \boxed{}$

Square

$d = s\sqrt{2} = 1.414s$

$A = s^2$

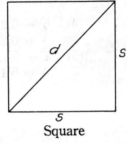

Square

Slide Rule Problem

(2) $s = 3.45$

$d = 1.414 \times 3.45 = \boxed{}$

$A = (3.45)^2 = \boxed{}$

Rectangle

$d = \sqrt{a^2 + b^2}$

Area $= A = ab$

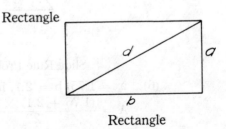

Rectangle

Slide Rule Problem

(3) a = 3.2, b = 5.7
d = $\sqrt{(3.2)^2 + (5.7)^2}$ = ◻
A = 3.2 × 5.7 = ◻

Parallelogram

Area = A = bh
= ab sin θ

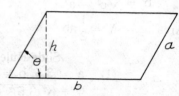

Parallelogram

Slide Rule Problems

(4) b = 6.2, h = 3.1
A = 6.2 × 3.1 = ◻
(5) a = 5.1, b = 7.2, θ = 35°
A = 5.1 × 7.2 × ◻ = ◻

Trapezoid

Area = $\dfrac{A = (a + b)h}{2}$

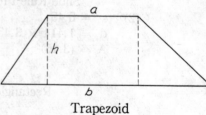

Trapezoid

Slide Rule Problem

(6) a = 1.75, b = 2.1, h = 2.8
A = $\dfrac{(1.75 + 2.1) \times 2.8}{2}$ = ◻

Trapezium

Area $= \dfrac{(H + h)a + bh + cH}{2}$

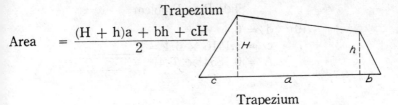

Trapezium

Slide Rule Problem

(7) a = 5.15, b = 0.5, c = 0.8
   H = 2.7, h = 1.8

$$A = \dfrac{(2.7 + 1.8)\,5.15 + 0.5 \times 1.8 + 0.8 \times 2.7}{2} = \boxed{}$$

Regular Polygon

Area $= A$
   $= \dfrac{\text{perimeter} \times r}{2}$

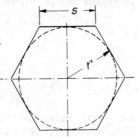

Regular Polygon

Slide Rule Problem

(8) Regular hexagon, where
   s = 2.08, r = 1.80

$$A = \dfrac{6 \times 2.08 \times 1.80}{2} = \boxed{}$$

Circle

Circumference $= c = \pi d$
   $= 3.1416\,d$

Area $= A = 0.7854 d^2$
   $= \pi r^2$
   $= \dfrac{c^2}{4\pi} = 0.7958 c^2$

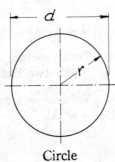

Circle

Slide Rule Problem

(9) $d = 6.4$
$c = 3.1416 \times 6.4 = \boxed{}$
$A = 0.7854 \times (6.4)^2 = \boxed{}$

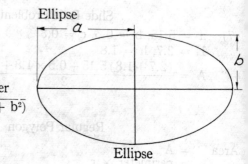

Area $= A = \pi ab$
        $= 3.1416ab$

Approximate perimeter
    $= p = \pi \sqrt{2(a^2 + b^2)}$

Ellipse

Slide Rule Problem

(10) $a = 3.2, \ b = 1.8$
$A = 3.1416 \times 3.2 \times 1.8 = \boxed{}$
$p = 3.1416 \sqrt{2[(3.2)^2 + (1.8)^2]} = \boxed{}$

PROBLEMS IN AREAS AND VOLUMES

Right Prism

Lateral surface = perimeter × height = Ph

Total surface = lateral surface plus two bases

Volume = area of base × height
    $= Ah$

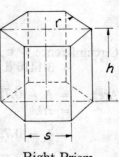

Right Prism

Slide Rule Problems

(1)   Right hexagonal prism, where
s = 1.15, h = 2.65, r = 0.498
Lateral surface = 6 × 1.15 × 2.65 = [＿＿＿＿＿]

Total surface = [＿＿＿＿＿] + $\dfrac{2 \times 6 \times 1.15 \times 0.498}{2}$

(See prob. 8,
Areas)   = [＿＿＿＿＿]

(2)   Volume =

$$\dfrac{6 \times 1.15 \times 0.498}{2} \times 2.65 = [＿＿＿＿＿]$$

Cylinder

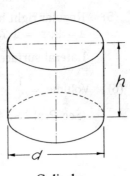

Lateral surface = πdh
Total surface = πdh plus two bases
Volume = $\dfrac{\pi d^2 h}{4}$
= 0.7854d²h

Cylinder

Slide Rule Problems

(3)   d = 2.1, h = 3.7
Lateral surface = 3.1416 × 2.1 × 3.7
= [＿＿＿＿＿]

(4)   Volume = 0.7854 × (2.1)² × 3.7
= [＿＿＿＿＿]

Right Pyramid

P = perimeter of base

A = area of base

Lateral surface = $\frac{1}{2}$ ps

Volume = $\frac{1}{3}$ Ah

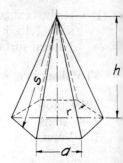

Right Pyramid

Slide Rule Problems

(5) Regular right hexagonal pyramid
a = 2, r = 1.732, h = 2.2, s = 2.8

Lateral surface = $\frac{1}{2} \times 2 \times 6 \times 2.8 = $ [   ]

(6) Volume = $\frac{1}{3} \times \frac{6 \times 2 \times 1.732}{2} \times 2.2 = $ [   ]

(See Prob. 8, Areas)

Cone

Height = h = $\sqrt{s^2 - r^2}$

Lateral surface = $\frac{\pi d}{2} \times s = 1.5708ds$

Volume = $\frac{\pi d^2 h}{12} = 0.2618d^2h$

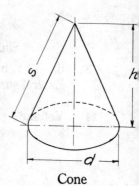

Cone

Slide Rule Problems

(7) d = 2.125, s = 3.07

$$h = \sqrt{(3.07)^2 - \left(\frac{2.125}{2}\right)^2} = \boxed{}$$

Lateral surface

$$= 1.5708 \times 2.125 \times 3.07$$

$$= \boxed{}$$

(8) Volume $= 0.2618 \times (2.125)^2 \times \boxed{} = \boxed{}$

Volume

$$= \frac{(2a + c)bh}{6}$$

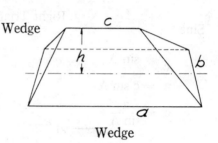

Wedge

Wedge

Slide Rule Problem

(9) a = 3.1, b = 2.6, c = 3.8, h = 3.7

$$\text{Volume} = \frac{(2 \times 3.1 + 3.8) \times 2.6 \times 3.7}{6}$$

$$= \boxed{}$$

Sphere

Surface $= \pi d^2$

Volume $= \frac{4}{3}\pi r^3$

$= 0.5236d^3$

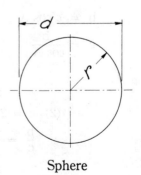

Sphere

Slide Rule Problems

(10) d = 2.04
Surface = 3.1416 × (2.04)²
= [_____]

(11) Volume =
0.5236 × (2.04)³ = [_____]

PROBLEMS IN TRIGONOMETRY

Right Triangles

Sine

$$\frac{a}{c} = \sin A$$

$$a = c \sin A$$

$$c = \frac{a}{\sin A}$$

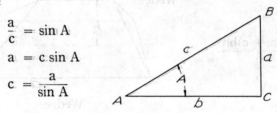

Slide Rule Problem

(1) a = 4.6, c = 8.1. Find angle A.

$$\frac{a}{c} = \sin A = \frac{4.6}{8.1} = [\quad\quad]$$

$$A = [\quad\quad]$$

Cosine

$$\frac{b}{c} = \cos A$$

$$b = c \cos A$$

$$c = \frac{b}{\cos A}$$

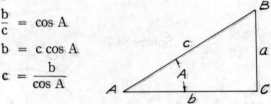

Slide Rule Problem

(2) c = 2.1, b = 1.732. Find angle A.

$$\frac{b}{c} = \cos A = \frac{1.732}{2.1} = [\quad\quad]$$

$$A = [\quad\quad]$$

Tangent

$$\frac{a}{b} = \tan A$$

$$a = b \tan A$$

$$b = \frac{a}{\tan A}$$

Slide Rule Problem

(3) a = 33.3, b = 102. Find angle A and side C.

$$\frac{a}{b} = \tan A = \frac{33.3}{102} = \boxed{}$$

$$A = \boxed{}$$

$$c = \frac{a}{\sin A} = \frac{33.3}{\sin \boxed{}} = \frac{33.3}{\boxed{}}$$

$$= \boxed{}$$

Oblique Triangles

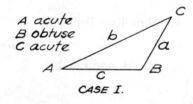

A acute
B obtuse
C acute

CASE I.

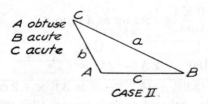

A obtuse
B acute
C acute

CASE II.

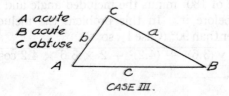

A acute
B acute
C obtuse

CASE III.

$$\frac{\sin A}{a} = \frac{\sin B}{b} = \frac{\sin C}{c}$$

$$\frac{a}{b} = \frac{\sin A}{\sin B}, \quad a = \frac{b \sin A}{\sin B}$$

$$\frac{b}{c} = \frac{\sin B}{\sin C}, \quad b = \frac{c \sin B}{\sin C}$$

$$\frac{c}{a} = \frac{\sin C}{\sin A}, \quad c = \frac{a \sin C}{\sin A}$$

$$a = \sqrt{b^2 + c^2 - 2bc \cos A}$$

$$b = \sqrt{a^2 + c^2 - 2ac \cos B}$$

$$c = \sqrt{a^2 + b^2 - 2ab \cos C}$$

$$\cos A = \frac{b^2 + c^2 - a^2}{2bc}$$

$$\cos B = \frac{a^2 + c^2 - b^2}{2ac}$$

$$\cos C = \frac{a^2 + b^2 - c^2}{2ab}$$

Slide Rule Problems

(4) $a = 3.6, c = 4.2, A = 35°, \sin A = 0.574$

Find angle C, angle B, and side b.

$$\frac{a}{c} = \frac{\sin A}{\sin C}$$

$$\frac{3.6}{4.2} = \frac{0.574}{\sin C} \quad \text{(Set up as a ratio.)}$$

$\sin C = \boxed{}$ $\quad C = \boxed{}$

$\angle B = 180° - \angle A - \angle C = \boxed{}$

$b = \sqrt{(3.6)^2 + (4.2)^2 - 2 \times 3.6 \times 4.2 \cos \boxed{}}$

When the included angle is greater than 90°, look up the cosine of 180° minus the included angle and put a minus sign before it. In this problem the included angle is greater than 90° (Case I), so

$b = \sqrt{(3.6)^2 + (4.2)^2 + 2 \times 3.6 \times 4.2 \cos \boxed{}}$

$\quad = \boxed{}$

(5) $c = 6.1$, $b = 5.7$, $A = 102°$, $\sin A = 0.978$, $\cos A = -0.208$.

Find side a, angle B, and angle C.

$a = \sqrt{(5.7)^2 + (6.1)^2 + 2 \times 5.7 \times 6.1 \times 0.208}$

$= \boxed{}$

$\dfrac{\text{Sin B}}{\text{Sin A}} = \dfrac{b}{a}$

$\dfrac{\text{Sin B}}{0.978} = \dfrac{5.7}{a}$ (Set up as a proportion.)

$\text{Sin B} = \boxed{}$ $\qquad B = \boxed{}$

$\angle C = 180° - \angle A - \angle B = \boxed{}$

PROBLEMS IN MECHANICS

Formulas for Moments

Moments clockwise = moments counterclockwise

$AF_1 = BF_2$

$\dfrac{A}{B} = \dfrac{F_2}{F_1}$

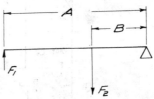

Slide Rule Problems

(1) $A = 5.5''$, $F_2 = 37.6$ lb, $B = 2.75''$
Find F_1

$\dfrac{5.5}{2.75} = \dfrac{37.6}{F_1}$, $F_1 = \boxed{}$ lb.

(2) $F_1 = 300$ lb, $B = 6''$, $A = 43''$
Find F_2

$\dfrac{F_2}{300} = \dfrac{43}{6}$, $F_2 = \boxed{}$ lb.

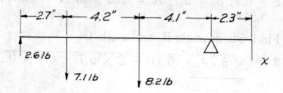

(3) Moments clockwise
2.6 (2.7 + 4.2 + 4.1) + 2.3x
Moments counterclockwise
7.1 (4.2 + 4.1) + (8.2 × 4.1)
So (2.6 × 11) + 2.3x = (7.1 × 8.3) + (8.2 × 4.1)

$$x = \frac{(7.1 \times 8.3) + (8.2 \times 4.1) - (2.6 \times 11)}{2.3}$$

= [＿＿＿＿] lb.

Formulas for Center of Gravity

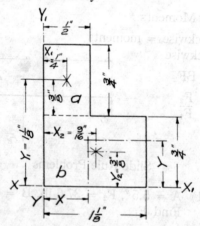

Since the center of gravity is the point at which the weight is concentrated, the center of gravity of a plate of uniform thickness and material may be found by taking moments about two axes at right angles to each other.

$$aY_1 + b\,Y_2 = AY$$
$$aX_1 + b\,X_2 = AX$$

Slide Rule Problems

(4)   Areas

$a = \frac{3}{4}'' \times \frac{1}{2}'' = \frac{3}{8}$ sq. in.

$b = 1\frac{1}{8}'' \times \frac{3}{4}'' = \frac{27}{32}$ sq. in.

Moments about $X - X_1$

$(\frac{3}{8} \times 1\frac{1}{8}) + (\frac{27}{32} \times \frac{3}{8}) = (\frac{3}{8} + \frac{27}{32}) Y$

$Y = \boxed{}$

(5)   Moments about $Y - Y_1$

$(\frac{3}{8} \times \frac{1}{4}) + (\frac{27}{32} \times \frac{9}{16}) = (\frac{3}{8} + \frac{27}{32}) X$

$X = \boxed{}$

Formulas for Gear Train

f = force to lift weight W (friction neglected)

$$F = W \times \frac{d_1 \times d_2 \times d_3}{D_1 \times D_2 \times D_3}$$

$$W = \frac{F \times D_1 \times D_2 \times D_3}{d_1 \times d_2 \times d_3}$$

When n_1 = speed of R_1

n_3 = speed of R_3

$$n_3 = \frac{n_1 \times D_1 \times D_2 \times D_3}{d_1 \times d_2 \times d_3}$$

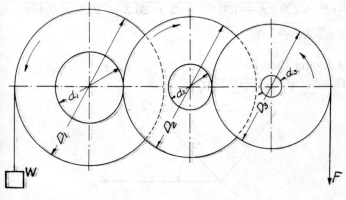

Slide Rule Problems

(6)   Given $D_1 = 12\frac{1}{2}''$, $D_2 = 10''$, $D_3 = 6\frac{1}{2}''$
    $d_1 = 5\frac{1}{2}''$, $d_2 = 3\frac{1}{2}''$, $d_3 = 2\frac{1}{2}''$
    $W = 2000$ lb.   Find F.

$$F = \frac{2000 \times 5.5 \times 3.5 \times 2.5}{12.5 \times 10 \times 6.5}$$

$$= \boxed{} \text{ lbs.}$$

(7)   If n_1 is to turn at 115 rpm, how fast will R_3 turn?

$$n_3 = \frac{115 \times 12.5 \times 10 \times 6.5}{5.5 \times 3.5 \times 2.5}$$

$$= \boxed{} \text{ rpm}$$

Formulas for Forces in a Plane

   θ less than 90°

$$F_3 = \sqrt{F_1{}^2 + F_2{}^2 + 2F_1 F_2 \cos \theta}$$

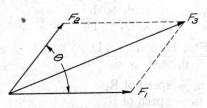

Slide Rule Problem

(8) $F_1 = 20.2$, $F_2 = 30.6$, $\theta = 62°$

$$F_3 = \sqrt{(20.2)^2 + (30.6)^2 + 2 \times 20.2 \times 30.6 \times 0.469}$$

$$= \boxed{}$$

θ greater than 90°

$$F_3 = \sqrt{F_1{}^2 + F_2{}^2 - 2F_1 F_2 \cos \theta}$$

Slide Rule Problem

(9) $F_1 = 3.1,\ F_2 = 4.7,\ \theta = 98°$

$$F_3 = \sqrt{(3.1)^2 + (4.7)^2 - 2 \times 3.1 \times 4.7 \times 0.139}$$

$$= \boxed{}$$

Formulas for Centrifugal Force

$$F = \frac{W V^2}{gR} = 0.000341\ WRn^2$$

$W =$ weight of body in pounds

$V =$ velocity of the revolving body in feet per second

$g =$ acceleration due to gravity $= 32.16$

$R =$ radius in feet of the circle in which the body revolves

$n =$ revolutions per minute

Slide Rule Problem

(10) What is the centrifugal force in pounds in a flywheel whose weight is concentrated in a rim that weighs 200 pounds and has a mean radius of 18 inches? The speed of the wheel is 150 rpm.

$$F = 0.000341 \times 200 \times \frac{18}{12} \times (150)^2$$

$$= \boxed{}$$

PROBLEMS IN CIVIL ENGINEERING

(1) Find the maximum bending moment (M) at the mid span of a beam supported at each end and carrying a uniform load. Use the formula

$$M = \frac{Wl}{8}$$

$W =$ total load $= 4000$ lb.

$l =$ length of beam between supports $= 8.5$ ft.

$M =$ bending moment in lb.-ft.

Substituting:

$$M = \frac{4000 \times 8.5}{8} = \boxed{}$$

(2) Find the deflection in inches of the beam in Problem 1. Use the formula

$$\Delta = - \frac{5}{384} \frac{Wl^3}{EI}$$

In the above formula l is in inches, E from a handbook is 29,000,000, and I = 6, so substituting:

$$\Delta = - \frac{5 \times 4000 \times (8.5 \times 12)^3}{384 \times 29,000,000 \times 6}$$

$$= - \frac{5 \times 4 \times (102)^3}{384 \times 29000 \times 6} = - \boxed{}$$

(3) Find the maximum bond stress between reinforcing steel and concrete from the formula,

$$u = \frac{V}{\Sigma_o \, j \, d}$$

u = bond in pounds per square inch
V = total shear = 10500 lb.
Σ_o = total perimeter of steel bars = 7.068″
j = 0.875 (from a handbook)
d = effective depth of beam = 18″
Substituting:

$$u = \frac{10500}{7.068 \times 0.875 \times 18} = \boxed{}$$

(4) Find the safe load in pounds for a pile driven with a drop-hammer, by using the following formula.

$$P = \frac{2wh}{S + 1}$$

W = weight of hammer in pounds = 2500 lb. for this problem
h = height that hammer drops = 9 ft. for this problem
S = average penetration per blow for the last few blows = 0.75 in. for this problem

Substituting:

$$P = \frac{2 \times 2500 \times 9}{0.75 + 1} = \boxed{}$$

(5) Compute the volume of earth between two parallel cross-sections from the formula

$$V = \frac{1}{2} \, l \, (A_1 + A_2)$$

l is in ft. and A_1 and A_2 are in square ft.

For this problem $l = 28$, $A_1 = 14$, $A_2 = 21.8$

Substituting:

$$V = \frac{1}{2} \times 28 \, (14 + 21.8) = \boxed{}$$

(6) Find the allowable stress in a column using the following formula.

$$f = \frac{18000}{1 + \frac{1}{18000} \left(\frac{l}{r}\right)^2} = \boxed{}$$

l is the length of the column in inches
r is the least radius of gyration (from a handbook)
f is the stress in pounds per square inch
In this prolem $l = 288$ inches, $r = 3.71$

Substituting:

$$f = \frac{18000}{1 + \frac{1}{18000} \left(\frac{288}{3.71}\right)^2} = \boxed{}$$

(7) Find the effective depth of the reinforcing steel in a concrete beam, using the formula

$$d = \sqrt{\frac{M}{Rb}}$$

M = 500,000 inch pounds (calculated in a manner similar to that in Problem 1)
R = 131 (from a handbook)
b = width of beam in inches = 12″ in this problem

Substituting:

$$d = \sqrt{\frac{500,000}{131 \times 12}} = \boxed{}$$

(8) Find the value of the Kutter Coefficient from the formula

$$C = \frac{1.49}{n} R^{\frac{1}{6}}$$

n = coefficient of roughness
R = hydraulic radius
In this problem $n = 0.017$, $R = 3.28$

Substituting:

$$C = \frac{1.49 \times (3.28)^{\frac{1}{6}}}{0.017} = \boxed{}$$

(9) The Francis Formula for flow over a submerged wier is

$$Q = 3.33 \, LH^{\frac{3}{2}}$$

where Q = quantity of water in cubic ft. per sec.

L = length of wier in ft.

H = height of water above crest of wier, usually measured about 6 ft. upstream from wier

In this problem L = 8.5 ft., H = 0.5 ft.

Substituting:

$$Q = 3.33 \times 8.5 \times (0.5)^{\frac{3}{2}} = \boxed{}$$

(10) Find the flow of water through a triangular wier from the formula

$$Q = 2.48 \, h^{\frac{5}{2}}$$

Q = quantity of water in cubic ft. per sec.

h = height of water above bottom of triangular notch

In this problem h = 1.5

Substituting:

$$Q = 2.48 \times (1.5)^{\frac{5}{2}} = \boxed{}$$

PROBLEMS IN CHEMISTRY

(1) A 0.500 gm. sample of a certain dye was bombed with Na_2O_2 and the S content thereby obtained as a sulfate. Upon the addition of an excess of $BaCl_2$, 0.4850 gm. of $BaSO_4$ were obtained in a tared gooch. Find the percentage of S in the original sample.

Solution. To find the weight of S in 0.4850 gm. of $BaSO_4$:

(1) Set up the relationship S ———→ $BaSO_4$

(2) Place corresponding atomic and molecular weights under each individual chemical concerned, thus:

S ———→ $BaSO_4$
32   233.4

which means each 32 gm. of S yields 233.4 gm. of $BaSO_4$.

(3) Next place the known weight and unknown weight over each individual chemical concerned, thus:

$$X \longrightarrow 0.4850$$

X	$\longrightarrow$	0.4850
S		$BaSO_4$
32		233.4

(4) Solve the proportion

$$\frac{X}{32} = \frac{0.4850}{233.4} \text{ or } X = \frac{32 \times 0.4850}{233.4}$$

In solving the above proportion for X the slide projects to the right, so the answer is 0.0665 gm. This problem can be solved directly by setting 0.4850 on C over 233.4 on D and over 32 on D reading 0.0665 on C. The first method makes the locating of the decimal point easier.

The percentage is, by regular slide rule division,

$$\frac{0.0665}{0.500} \times 100 = \boxed{}$$

(2) Find the number of liters of oxygen to burn 20 gm. of coal.
Solution. $C + O_2 = CO_2$ and since for all practical purposes, the gram molecular weight of any gas occupies 22.4 liters, write the atomic or the molecular weight under the solid or liquid chemical individuals and 22.4 liters under the gaseous chemical individual, thus:

$$\begin{array}{ccc} C & + & O_2 & = CO_2 \\ 12 & & 22.4 \end{array}$$

Place the known weight and unknown weight over the chemical individual concerned.

$$\begin{array}{ccc} 24 & & X \\ C & + & O_2 & = CO_2 \\ 12 & & 22.4 \end{array}$$

Solve $\dfrac{24}{12} = \dfrac{X}{22.4}$

Over 12 on D set 24 on C; over 22.4 on D read the answer on C.

(3) The percentage of oxygen in air by volume is 20.8. Find the number of liters of air to supply 50 liters of oxygen.

Solution.
Liters of air $\times$ 0.208 = liters of oxygen required.

So   liters of air $\times 0.208 = 50$

or   liters of air $= \dfrac{50}{0.208} = \boxed{}$

(4) 250 cc. of CO_2 were obtained at 15°C and 750 mm. of Hg. Find the volume at standard conditions: that is, 0°C and 760 mm. of Hg.

Solution. Use the equation $\dfrac{P_0 V_0}{T_0} = \dfrac{P_1 V_1}{T_1}$

where P_0 = pressure under which V_0 cc. of gas exist at T_0 absolute temperature

T_0 = degrees Centigrade + 273

In the problem $P_0 = 750$ mm. $P_1 = 760$

$V_0 = 250$ cc. $V_1 = ?$

$T_0 = 15° + 273° = 288°$ $T_1 = 273$

Solve equation for the unknown V_1.

$V_1 = \dfrac{P_0 \, V_0 \, T_1}{T_0 \, P_1}$

$= \dfrac{750 \times 250 \times 273}{288 \times 760}$

$= \boxed{}$

(5) Find the pressure at which a liter of HOH will dissolve 0.4 gm. of H_2 at 0°C.

Solution. Use Henry's Law, which states that if the temperature remains constant, the weight of gas dissolved is directly proportional to the pressure of the gas.

As an equation $\dfrac{P_0}{W_0} = \dfrac{P_1}{W_1}$

From a table the solubility of H_2 in HOH is 0.00193 gm. per liter, so $\dfrac{1}{0.00193} = \dfrac{P_1}{0.4}$

Over 193 on D set 1 on C; over 4 on D read the value of P_1 on C.

(6) Calculate the weight of Aq deposited from a solution of Aq NO_3 by 0.25 amperes for 1 hour.

Solution. 1 Faraday = 96500 coulombs = quantity of electricity necessary to deposit 1 gm. equivalent of any ion.

The gram equivalent is the atomic weight of the ion divided by its charge. For example, $Aq = \dfrac{107.88}{1}$, $Cu = \dfrac{63.5}{2}$

The coulombs = amperes times seconds.
So   coulombs = $0.25 \times 60 \times 60 = 900$ and since 96500 coulombs deposit 107.88 gm. of Aq, 900 coulombs will deposit $\dfrac{107.88 \times 900}{96500} = \boxed{}$

(7) Find the normality of a solution.
Solution.   Normality may be defined as the gram equivalents of a material in a liter of HOH. To standardize or find the normality of a solution it is only necessary to titrate the material against a known weight of pure material. For example, if $NaCO_3$ were taken as the pure material and methyl orange as the indicator, then since the molecular weight of $NaCO_3 = 106$ and since there are 2 + ions, the equivalent weight of $NaCO_3 = 53$. This means a liter of $NaCO_3$ would contain 53 gm. and a cubic centimeter, 0.053 gm. If $25 \times 0.053 = 1.325$ gm. of pure $NaCO_3$ be weighed out, 1.325 gm. of $NaCO_3$ would react with exactly 1 N of any kind of acid.
Suppose it required 24.5 cc. of the HCL solution to react with the 1.325 gm. of $NaCO_3$. The normality could then be found as $25 \times 1 = 24.5 \times N$

$$N = \frac{25}{24.5} = \boxed{}$$

(8) Find the normality of the HCL solution, when 25 cc. of 1.02 N solution react with 24.6 cc. of HCL of unknown normality.

Solution.   cc. $\times$ N = cc. $\times$ N
$\qquad\quad 25 \times 1.02 = 24.6 \times N$

$$N = \frac{25 \times 1.02}{24.6} = \boxed{}$$

(9) Find the number of cubic centimeters of 1.022 N HCL to make 500 cc. of 0.1 N HCL.

Solution.

$$\begin{aligned}
\text{cc.} \times \text{N} &= \text{cc.} \times \text{N} \\
\text{cc.} \times 1.022 &= 500 \times 0.1 \\
\text{cc.} &= \frac{500 \times 0.1}{1.022} = \frac{50}{1.022} = \boxed{}
\end{aligned}$$

(10) Calculate the pH of a 0.1 N solution of acetic acid.

Solution.

$$pH = \log_{10} \frac{1}{C_H}$$

0.1 N acetic acid is 1.3% ionized.

Therefore the C_H of 0.1 N acetic acid $= 0.1 \times 0.13 = 0.013$ moles per liter.

$$pH = \log_{10} \frac{1}{0.013} = \log_{10} 76.9 = \boxed{}$$

or since $0.013 = 1.3 \times 10^{-2}$

$$pH = \log_{10} \frac{1}{1.3 \times 10^{-2}} = \log_{10} \frac{10^2}{1.3}$$
$$= \log 100 - \log 1.3$$
$$= 2 - 0.116 = \boxed{}$$

PROBLEMS IN ELECTRICAL ENGINEERING

(1) The resistance of a copper wire is approximately $R = \dfrac{10.8\,l}{d^2}$

where R is in ohms, l is in feet, and d is the diameter of the wire in mils (thousandths of an inch).

What is the diameter of a wire 528 feet long and 0.102 inches in diameter?

Solution. 0.102 inches $= 102$ mils, so

$$R = \frac{10.8 \times 528}{(102)^2} = \boxed{} \text{ ohms}$$

(2) The reactance X_L in ohms of a circuit is $X_L = 2\pi fL$, where $2\pi = 6.2832+$, f is the frequency of the alternating current, and L is the inductance of the circuit in henrys. What is the reactance of a circuit to 60 cycle current if the inductance of the circuit is 0.218 henrys?

Solution.

$$X_L = 2\pi fL = 6.2832 \times 60 \times 0.218 = \boxed{} \text{ ohms}$$

(3) The impedance Z in ohms of a circuit can be represented by the hypotenuse of a right triangle when the base represents the resistance R in ohms, and the altitude the reactance X in ohms.

What is the impedance of a circuit whose resistance is 20.8 ohms and whose reactance is 17.6 ohms?

Solution.
$$Z = \sqrt{R^2 + X^2} = \sqrt{(20.8)^2 + (17.6)^2} = \boxed{} \text{ ohms}$$

(4) The inductive reactance X_L of a circuit varies directly with the frequency.

What will be the reactance of a circuit on 55 cycles, if its reactance on 60 cycles is 0.26 ohms?

Solution.
$$X_{55} = X_{60} \times \frac{f_{55}}{f_{60}} = 0.26 \times \frac{55}{60} = \boxed{} \text{ ohms}$$

(5) In a circuit containing only capacity, the reactance $X_C = \dfrac{1}{2\pi fC}$, where C is the capacity in farads. As capacitance is usually measured in microfarads the formula becomes $X_C = \dfrac{10^6}{2\pi fC}$.

What is the capacity reactance of a circuit containing a capacitor of 12 mf. if used on a 1000 cycle circuit?

Solution.
$$X_C = \frac{10^6}{2\pi fC} = \frac{10^6}{6.2832 \times 1000 \times 12} = \boxed{} \text{ ohms}$$

(6) In calculating the temperature of a coil in degrees Centigrade from measurements of resistance, the following formula is used.

$$\frac{R_h}{R_c} = \frac{234.5 + T_h}{234.5 + T_c}$$

R_h and R_c are the resistances hot and cold, and T_h and T_c are the temperatures hot and cold.

A transformer has a cold resistance of 1.3 ohms, having stood in a room whose temperature is 25°C. After being in service for about two hours its resistance is 1.38 ohms. What is its temperature?

Solution.

$$\frac{1.38}{1.3} = \frac{234.5 + T_h}{234.5 + 25} = \frac{234.5 + T_h}{259.5} = \boxed{} \text{ deg. C}$$

The above proportion gives $234.5 + T_h$. Subtract 234.5 to get T_h.

(7) The turns on a transformer are calculated from the formula

$N = \dfrac{10^8 E}{4.44\phi f}$, where E is the effective voltage, ϕ the

total magnetic flux, and f the frequency.

How many turns will be required for a transformer that is to run on a 120 volt, 60 cycle circuit if the flux is 40,000 lines?

Solution.

$$N = \frac{10^8 \times 120^2}{4.44 \times 40,000 \times 60} = \frac{10,000}{8.88} = \boxed{} \text{ turns}$$

(8) It is customary to allow about 10,000 lines of magnetic flux to every square centimeter of cross section of the core of a transformer and to assume that the net cross section is about 0.9 the gross cross section, since some space is taken up by the insulating varnish on the laminations.

What would be the flux in a core whose cross section measures $1.5'' \times 1.75''$?

Solution.

Flux $= \phi = 1.5 \times 1.75 \times 2.54 \times 2.54 \times 0.9 \times 10,000$

$= \boxed{}$ lines

(9) If the primary of a transformer has 264 turns and the secondary 187 turns, what is the secondary no-load voltage when the primary voltage is 55 volts?

Solution.

$$\frac{55}{X} = \frac{264}{187} \qquad X = \boxed{} \text{ volts}$$

(10) What will be the resistance of a coil of #28 d.c.c. copper wire, when wound on the spool shown by the sketch, assuming that the wires are wound close together?

Diam. of #28 d.c.c. over insulation $= 0.0206''$.

Resistance per 1000 ft. $= 64.9$ ohms.

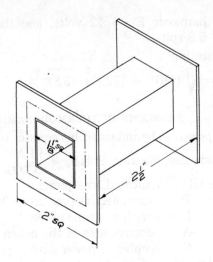

Solution. From the sketch the mean length of a turn of wire is shown by the dotted line and is

$$\left(\frac{2'' + 1\frac{1}{8}''}{2}\right) \times 4 = 6.25''$$

The turns per layer $= \dfrac{2.5''}{.0206''}$

The number of layers $= \dfrac{\frac{1}{2}\,(2'' - 1\frac{1}{8}'')}{0.0206} = \dfrac{0.5 \times 0.875}{0.0206}$

The number of turns $N = \dfrac{2.5}{0.0206} \times \dfrac{0.5 \times 0.875}{0.0206}$

The number of feet of wire $= \dfrac{2.5 \times 0.5 \times 0.875}{0.0206 \times 0.0206} \times \dfrac{6.25}{12}$

The resistance is

$$R = \frac{2.5 \times 0.5 \times 0.875 \times 6.25 \times 64.9}{0.0206 \times 0.0206 \times 12 \times 1000} = \boxed{} \text{ ohms}$$

(11) When a wave of E.M.F contains harmonics, the effective valve of the wave is

$$E = \sqrt{E_1^2 + E_3^2 + E_5^2 + \ldots E_n^2}$$

Using the above formula find the effective value of a wave of E.M.F. whose fundamental is $E_1 = 110$ volts, the third harmonic E_3 = 22 volts, and the fifth harmonic E_5 = 5.8 volts.

Substituting:

$$E = \sqrt{(110)^2 + (22)^2 + (5.8)^2} = \boxed{} \text{ volts}$$

PROBLEMS IN THERMODYNAMICS

(1) *Horsepower.* The indicated horsepower of an engine from the indicator diagram is $HP_i = \dfrac{PLAN}{33000}$

where HP_i = indicated horsepower

      P = mean effective pressure in lb. per square inch

      L = length of stroke in feet

      A = effective area of the piston in square inches

      N = number of power strokes per minute

Calculate the indicated horsepower of a 12″ diameter by 13″ stroke steam engine which operates at a speed of 265 rpm. The mean effective pressure of the head end is 27.5 lb. per sq. in. and of the crank end 27.8 lb. per sq. in. The diameter of the piston rod is 1⅝″.

Solution. Head end.

    Area piston = 0.7854 × (12)² = 113 sq. in.

$$HP = \frac{27.5 \times 113 \times 13 \times 265}{33000 \times 12} = \boxed{} \text{ HP}$$

      Crank end. Area piston = 113 sq. in.

    Area piston rod .7854 × (1⅝)² = 2.07

        Effective area piston = 110.93

$$HP = \frac{27.8 \times 110.93 \times 13 \times 265}{33000 \times 12} = \boxed{}$$

        Total indicated HP = $\boxed{}$

(2) The brake horsepower from a Prony (friction) brake is

$$HP_b = \frac{2\pi \, PLN}{33000}$$

where HP_b = brake horsepower

    2π = 6.2832

     P = net pull at end of brake arm in pounds

     L = length of brake arm in feet

     N = revolutions per minute

Calculate the brake horsepower of an engine as measured by a Prony brake, when the effective pull is 32 lb. and the speed 250 rpm. The length of the lever arm is 32 inches.

Solution.

$$HP_b = \frac{6.2832 \times 32 \times 32 \times 250}{33000 \times 12} = \boxed{\qquad} \ HP$$

(3) *Gas Constant.*

$$PV = WRT$$

where   P = absolute pressure in pounds per square foot
        V = volume in cubic feet
        W = weight of gas in pounds
        R = gas constant for 1 pound of gas in foot-pound system of units (R = 53.3 for air)
        T = temperature in degrees F absolute

What is the weight of 2 cubic feet of air at 14.4 lbs. per sq. in. absolute pressure and 70° F?

Solution.

$$14.4 \times 144 \times 2 = W \times 53.3 \times (460 + 70)$$
$$W = \boxed{\qquad}$$

(4) *Isothermal Energy Change in Gas.*

$$W = w R T \log_\epsilon r$$

where   W = work in foot-pounds
        w = weight of gas in pounds
        R = gas constant in foot-pound system of units
        T = temperature in degrees F absolute
        r = ratio of expansion $\left(\dfrac{V_2}{V_1}; \text{i.e.,} \dfrac{\text{final volume}}{\text{initial volume}}\right)$

Three pounds of air at 32 degrees F and atmospheric pressure are compressed to 4 atmospheres absolute. What is the work of compression if the compression is isothermal?

Solution.

Here   r = ratio of compression $= \dfrac{V_2}{V_1} = \dfrac{P_1}{P_2} = \dfrac{1}{4}$

$$\log_\epsilon r = \log_\epsilon \tfrac{1}{4} = - \log_\epsilon 4 = - 1.3863$$
Then $W = 3 \times 53.3 \times (460+32) \times (-1.3863) = - \boxed{\qquad} \ \text{ft.-lbs.}$

Note: The minus sign indicates compression.

(5) *Adiabatic Energy Change in Gas*.

$$W = \frac{wR(T_1 - T_2)}{k-1}$$

where W = work in foot-pounds

w = weight of gas in pounds

R = gas constant in foot-pound system of units

T_1 = initial temperature in degrees F absolute

T_2 = final temperature in degrees F absolute

k = $\frac{c_p}{c_v}$ $\left(\text{i.e., } \frac{\text{specific heat at constant pressure}}{\text{specific heat at constant volume}} \right)$

For air $c_p = 0.2375$, $c_v = 0.169$, and k = 1.405

Two pounds of air are expanded from a temperature of 300 degrees F to 200 degrees F adiabatically. How many foot-pounds of work are developed?

Solution. Since T_1 and T_2 appear in a difference, either degrees F or degrees F absolute may be used.

$$W = \frac{2 \times 53.3 \times (300-200)}{1.405-1} = \frac{2 \times 53.3 \times 100}{0.405} = \boxed{\qquad} \text{ ft-lbs.}$$

Note: The plus sign indicates expansion.

(6) *Adiabatic Expansion* (*or Compression*) *of a Gas*

$$T_2 = T_1 \left(\frac{P_2}{P_1} \right)^{\frac{k-1}{k}} \quad \text{or} \quad \frac{T_2}{T_1} = \left(\frac{P_2}{P_1} \right)^{\frac{k-1}{k}}$$

where T_2 = final temperature in degrees F absolute

T_1 = initial temperature in degrees F absolute

P_2 = final pressure in pounds per square inch absolute

P_1 = initial pressure in pounds per square inch absolute

k = ratio of specific heats (as in 5)

Air at 15 pounds per square inch absolute and 100 degrees F is compressed adiabatically in a non-flow process to 200 pounds per square inch absolute. What is the final temperature?

Solution. Since P_1 and P_2 appear in a ratio, either pounds per square inch or pounds per square foot may be used.

$$T_2 = (460 + 100) \times \left(\frac{200}{15}\right)^{\frac{1.405 - 1}{1.405}}$$

$$560 \times (13.33)^{0.288} \boxed{\qquad} = \text{degrees F absolute}$$

$$\text{or} = \boxed{-460} \text{ degrees. F}$$

(7) *Efficiency of the Ideal or Air Standard Otto Cycle*

$$\epsilon = 1 - \left(\frac{1}{r}\right)^{k-1} = 1 - \frac{1}{r^{k-1}}$$

where ϵ = efficiency

  r = compression ratio

  $\left(\dfrac{V_a}{B_b} : \text{i.e.,} \dfrac{\text{volume before compression}}{\text{volume after compression}}\right)$

  k = ratio of specific heats (as in 5)

In an Otto cycle, $V_a = 13.5$ and $V_b = 2.134$. What is the efficiency of the cycle?

Solution. $r = \dfrac{V_a}{V_b} = \dfrac{13.5}{2.134}$

$$\epsilon = 1 - \left(\frac{2.134}{13.5}\right)^{1.405 - 1}$$

$$= 1 - (0.1581)^{0.405} = \boxed{\qquad} \%$$

(8) *Efficiency of the Diesel Cycle.*

$$\epsilon = 1 - \frac{1}{k}\left(\frac{T_d - T_a}{T_c - T_b}\right)$$

where ϵ = efficiency

  k = ratio of specific heats (as in 5)

  T_d = temperature at end of expansion in degrees F absolute

  T_a = temperature at beginning of compression in degrees F absolute

  T_c = temperature at beginning of expansion in degrees F absolute

  T_b = temperature at end of compression in degrees F absolute

In a Diesel cycle, the temperatures are as follows:

At beginning of compression,	70 degrees F
At end of compression,	985 degrees F
At beginning of expansion,	2485 degrees F
At end of expansion,	975 degrees F

What is the efficiency?

Solution. Since all temperatures appear as differences, either degrees F or degrees F absolute may be used.

$$\epsilon = 1 - \frac{1}{1.405} \left(\frac{975 - 70}{2485 - 985} \right)$$

$$= 1 - \left(\frac{1}{1.405} \times \frac{905}{1500} \right) = \boxed{} \%$$

(9) *Vapor Flow from a Nozzle*

$$V = 223.8 \sqrt{h_1 - h_2}$$

where V = velocity in feet per second

h_1 = initial enthalpy in B.T.U. per pound

h_2 = final enthalpy in B.T.U. per pound

Steam at 300 pounds per square inch absolute and 560 degrees F is supplied to a turbine nozzle which discharges against 60 pounds per square inch absolute. What is the discharge velocity?

Solution. From steam tables we find

h_1 = 1291.9 B.T.U. per pound

By calculation we find

h_2 = 1152.5

V = $223.8 \sqrt{1291.9 - 1152.5}$

= $223.8 \sqrt{139.4}$ = $\boxed{}$ feet per second

(10) *Air Flow through an Orifice*

(By Fliegner's Empirical Formula)

$$w = \frac{0.53 \, f \, A \, P_1}{\sqrt{T_1}} \quad \text{(when } P_1 \text{ is greater than } 2 \, P_2\text{)}$$

where w = weight of gas in pounds per second

f = coefficient of discharge, determined by experiment

A = area of orifice in square feet

P_1 = initial pressure in pounds per square foot absolute

P_2 = final pressure in pounds per square foot absolute

T_1 = initial temperature in degrees F absolute

Air at 100 pounds per square inch absolute and at 70 degrees F flows through an orifice whose area is 0.5 square inch and against a discharge pressure of 35 pounds per square inch absolute. The coefficient of discharge of the orifice is 0.62.

What is the weight of gas discharged per second?

Solution. Here $P_1 = 100$, $P_2 = 35$, $P_1 > 2P_2$, so the formula is applicable.

$$w = 0.530 \times 0.62 \times \frac{0.5}{144} \times \frac{100}{\sqrt{460 + 70}}$$

$$= \boxed{} \text{ pounds per second}$$

ANSWERS TO PROBLEMS IN PART I

ANSWERS—Page 9

1. = 4.1
2. = 9.8
3. = 9.8
4. = 18.9
5. = 450
6. = 12.7
7. = 14.4
8. = 1.45
9. = 1048
10. = 10.35

ANSWERS—Page 10

1. = 3.2
2. = 269
3. = 2.64
4. = 17.3
5. = 0.14
6. = 135
7. = 5.02
8. = 0.0387
9. = 16.25
10. = 0.043

ANSWERS—Page 16

2. = 9.50
3. = 865
4. = 133.1
5. = 671

ANSWERS—Pages 16 and 17

1. = 0.64
2. = 178
3. = 0.0000324
4. = 1742
5. = 27800

ANSWERS—Page 19

1. = 5500
2. = 0.930
3. = 0.184
4. = 0.694
5. = 0.0312
6. = 582
7. = 164
8. = 0.00025
9. = 0.144
10. = 0.0255

ANSWERS—Page 33

1. = 53.4
2. = 194
3. = 2.13
4. = 404

ANSWERS—Page 38

1. = 53.2
2. = 16.8
3. = 8.29
4. = 24.8
5. = 4.31
6. = 1.97

ANSWERS TO PROBLEMS FOR DRILL

MULTIPLICATION—Page 105

1. 1820
2. 4.22
3. 0.000117
4. 0.00568
5. 6.67
6. 0.009796
7. 1370
8. 142,000
9. 865
10. 133.1

DIVISION—Page 105

1. 6.97
2. 0.0258
3. 8.14
4. 55,600
5. 0.00000939
6. 1.12
7. 0.149
8. 18840
9. 0.1083
10. 0.000254

COMBINED MULTIPLICATION AND DIVISION—Page 106

1. 19.1
2. 0.565
3. 102.5
4. 0.333
5. 0.144
6. 1.444
7. 0.0193
8. 109,100,000
9. 0.000837
10. 0.00000000571

RECIPROCALS—Page 107

1. 0.357
2. 0.0345
3. 0.00353
4. 0.0001044
5. 0.000935
6. 16
7. 769
8. 3570
9. 10,870
10. 345,000

SQUARING NUMBERS—Page 107

1. 14.44
2. 2725
3. 627000
4. 0.00270
5. 0.1018
6. 7.29
7. 462
8. 30,600
9. 0.0001823
10. 0.04326

SQUARE ROOT—Page 108

1. 18.79
2. 34.5
3. 0.0801
4. 0.0735
5. 0.0224
6. 0.0775
7. 0.286
8. 144.6
9. 980
10. 100.1

CUBING NUMBERS—Page 108

1. 227
2. 0.4219
3. 0.0001406
4. 68,920
5. 0.00002979
6. 0.01065
7. 91.13
8. 1405
9. 0.008615
10. 6.859

CUBE ROOT—Page 109

1. = 5.325
2. = 6.316
3. = 9.963
4. = 4.61
5. = 0.2714
6. = 0.4481
7. = 0.6768
8. = 0.3141
9. = 0.1458
10. = 0.0677

SINES—Page 109

1. = 0.616
2. = 0.182
3. = 0.09
4. = 0.0523
5. = 0.0436
6. = 0.01164
7. = 0.00436
8. = 0.01047
9. = 0.0000582
10. = 0.000145

COSINES—Page 110

1. = 0.342
2. = 0.643
3. = 0.866
4. = 0.940
5. = 0.976
6. = 0.174
7. = 0.938
8. = −0.872
9. = −0.866
10. = 0.764

TANGENTS—Page 110

1. = 0.933
2. = 0.795
3. = 0.424
4. = 0.277
5. = 0.176
6. = 0.105
7. = 0.0524
8. = −3.49
9. = −1.00
10. = −0.176

COTANGENTS—Page 111

1. = 1.327
2. = 1.511
3. = 2.23
4. = 3.27
5. = 5.67
6. = 9.51
7. = −1.192
8. = 0.364
9. = −0.176
10. = 5.67

LOGARITHMS—Page 111

1. = 585
2. = 97.0
3. = 2.15
4. = 0.15
5. = 0.0029
6. = 2.465
7. = 1.884
8. = 0.944
9. = 9.813—10
10. = 7.961—10

POWERS AND ROOTS—Pages 111-112

1. = 18.3
2. = 4240
3. = 4000
4. = 0.283
5. = 0.24
6. = 13.3
7. = 3.77
8. = 59,000
9. = 0.282
10. = 0.182

ANSWERS TO PRACTICAL PROBLEMS

AREAS—Pages 113-116

1. c = 5.47   A = 7.35
2. d = 4.88   A = 11.9
3. d = 6.54   A = 18.24
4. A = 19.22
5. A = 21.06
6. A = 5.39
7. A = 13.12
8. A = 11.23
9. c = 20.11   A = 32.17
10. A = 18.096   p = 16.31

AREAS AND VOLUMES—Pages 116-120

1. Lateral surface = 18.285   Total surface = 21.72
2. Volume = 4.55
3. Lateral surface = 24.41
4. Volume = 12.81
5. Lateral surface = 16.8
6. Volume = 7.62
7. Height = 2.88   Lateral surface = 10.25
8. Volume = 3.40
9. Volume = 16.03
10. Surface = 13.07
11. Volume = 4.445

TRIGONOMETRY—Pages 120-123

1. Sin A = .5679   Angle A = 34° 36′
2. Cos A = .8248   Angle A = 34° 26′
3. Tan A = .3265   Angle A = 18° 5′ side c = 107.3
4. Sin C = 0.6697   Angle C = 42°   Angle B = 103°
   side b = 6.12
5. Side a = 9.17   Sin B = 0.608   Angle B = 37° 30′
   Angle C = 40° 30′

MECHANICS—Pages 123-127

1. 18.8 lb.
2. 2150 lb.
3. 27.8 lb. clockwise
4. Y = 0.606
5. X = 0.466
6. 118.5 lb.
7. 1941.6 rpm
8. 43.87
9. 5.26
10. 2302 lb.

CIVIL ENGINEERING—Pages 127-130

1. 4250 lb.-ft.
2. 0.3176 inch
3. 94.3 lb. per sq. in.
4. 25,714 lb.
5. 501 cu. ft.
6. 13,500 lb. per sq. in.
7. 17.8 inches
8. 106.8
9. 9.99 cu. ft. per sec.
10. 6.84 cu. ft. per sec.

CHEMISTRY—Pages 130-134

1. 13.3%
2. 44.8 gm.
3. 240 liters
4. 234 cc.
5. 207
6. 1.006 gm.
7. 1.02
8. 1.04
9. 48.9
10. 1.886

ELECTRICAL ENGINEERING—Pages 134-138

1. 0.548 ohms
2. 82.18 ohms
3. 27.25 ohms
4. 0.2383 ohm
5. 13.26 ohms
6. 40.97 degrees C
7. 1126 turns
8. 152,400 lines
9. 38.96 volts
10. 87.12 ohms
11. 112.3 volts

THERMODYNAMICS—Pages 138-143

1. 53.86 HP_i
2. 4.06 HP_b
3. 0.1468 lb.
4. −109,200 ft.-lb.
5. 26,300 ft.-lb.
6. 721 degrees F
7. 52.6%
8. 57.1%
9. 2643 ft. per sec.
10. 0.00496 lb. per sec.